MARVEL® MASTERS
THE TALES OF KURT BUSIEK

MARVEL MASTERS
THE TALES OF KURT BUSIEK

WRITER: KURT BUSIEK

ARTISTS:
POWER MAN AND IRON FIST #98-100
ERNIE CHAN
MARVELS #0
ALEX ROSS
UNTOLD TALES OF SPIDER-MAN #21
PAT OLLIFFE
IRON MAN VOL.3 #1
SEAN CHEN
THUNDERBOLTS VOL.1 #10-12
MARK BAGLEY
THOR: GODSTORM #1
STEVE RUDE

INKERS: ANDY MUSHYNSKY, MIKE MIGNOLA, AL WILLIAMSON, ERIC CANNON, VINCE RUSSELL, SCOTT HANNA, LARRY MAHLSTADT, GREG ADAMS, MIKE ROYER

COLOURISTS: BOB SHAREN, CHRISTIE STEEL, ALEX ROSS, STEVE MATTSSON, LIQUID!, JOE ROSAS, GREG WRIGHT

LETTERERS: JANICE CHIANG, RICHARD STARKINGS, COMICRAFT'S DAVE LANPHEAR, JOHN COSTANZA

COVER ART: ALEX ROSS

ASSISTANT EDITORS: SPENCER LAMM, MARC SUMERAK

EDITORS: DENNY O'NEIL, MARC McLAURIN, TOM BREVOORT, BOBBIE CHASE,

MARVEL® presents: **MARVEL MASTERS: THE TALES OF KURT BUSIEK**

MARVEL MASTERS: THE TALES OF KURT BUSIEK. Contains material originally published in magazine form as Power Man And Iron Fist #98-100, Marvels #0, Untold Tales of Spider-Man #21, Iron Man Volume 3 #1, Thunderbolts Volume 1 #10-12 and Thor: Godstorm #1. Published by Panini Publishing, a division of Panini UK Limited. Mike Riddell, Managing Director. Alan O'Keefe, Managing Editor. Mark Irvine, Production Manager. Marco M. Lupoi, Publishing Director Europe. Brady Webb, Reprint Editor. Tim Warran-Smith, Designer. Office of publication: Panini House, Coach & Horses Passage, The Pantiles, Tunbridge Wells, Kent TN2 5UJ. Tel: 01892 500 100. First printing 2008 Printed in Italy.
ISBN: 978-1-905239-74-0

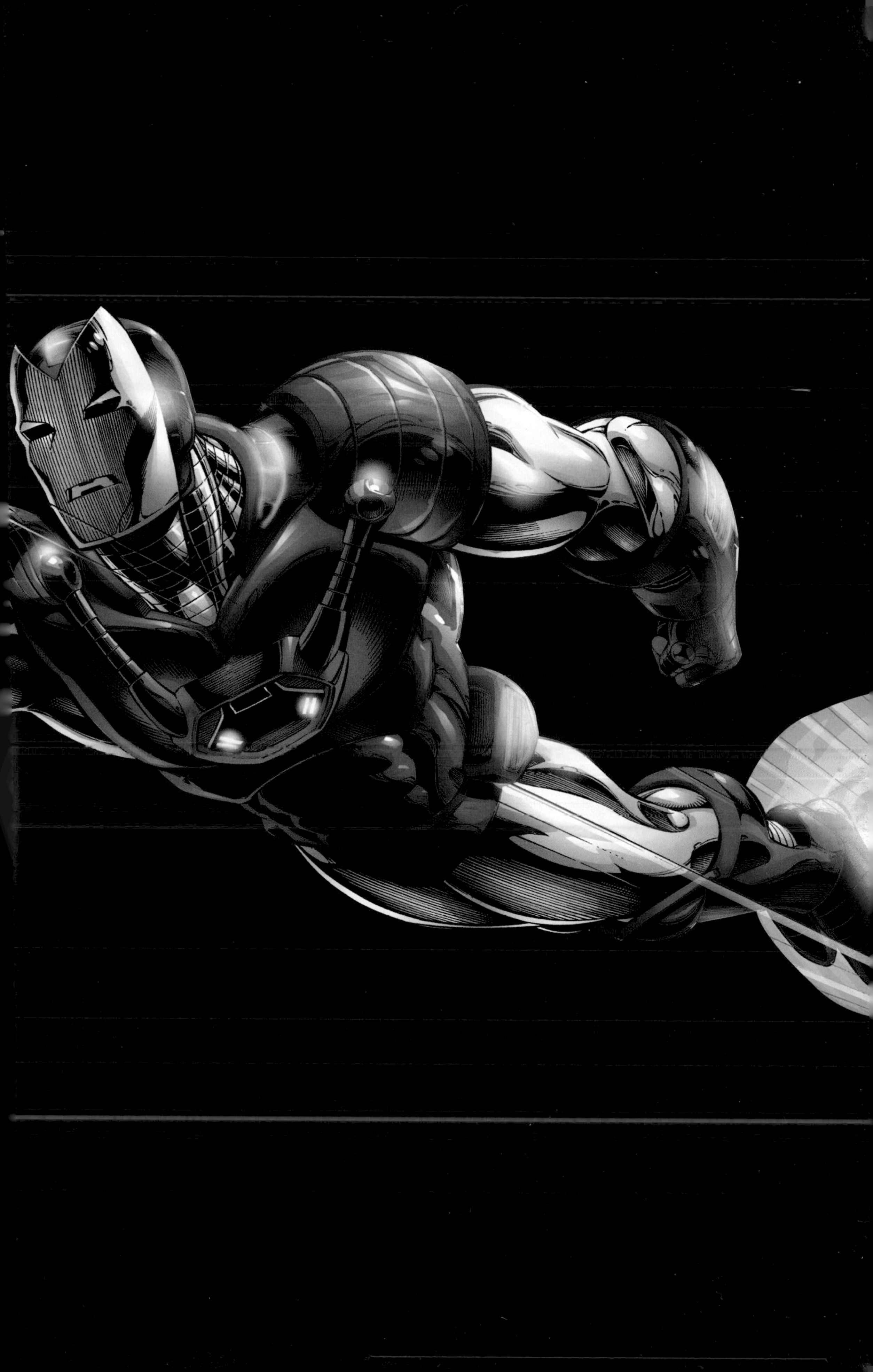

INTRODUCTION BY GEORGE PÉREZ

First, let's get one thing straight about the man called Busiek: it rhymes with "Music". There now, if I've done nothing else in this introduction at least I've allowed you to read this book with the ability to "hear" his name pronounced correctly. I know, it's a small detail, but detail has always been a major cornerstone of my art style – and an eye for detail is something that Kurt and I have in common.

I first encountered Kurt's work on the magnificent **Marvels** mini-series, where he and painter-extraordinaire **Alex Ross** brought a new perspective to the birth of the Marvel Universe. From the first appearance of the original Human Torch, to the death of Gwen Stacy, Kurt revisited the major touchstones of the early Marvel era through a first-person perspective that had us all vicariously reliving the awe and wonder that I felt when I first encountered those original stories. And a huge part of that sense of wonder was attributable to Kurt's incredible sense of detail.

Quite simply, Kurt knows his comics history. He embraces it and respects it. Hell, the guy loves it! It informs every comic story he writes. But, and this is a big but, never at the expense of creating something new. He doesn't live in the past, simply recycling the old stories that inspired him. Kurt has the uncanny ability to find a new take on an old plot point, a novel approach to an often arcane bit of detail that spins out into a new story that becomes more than a homage to the past. It becomes something totally original. One needs only to read the last page of his **Thunderbolts** series or the many issues of **The Avengers** that I was lucky enough to illustrate to understand what I mean. I absolutely loved the attention Kurt had for every little detail of Avengers history that he incorporated into the series. Man, the reference pile that he provided for every issue was both intimidating and inspiring. Kurt just made me want to work even harder to make sure I squeezed in every story facet I could into our allotted pages – and then add even more.

And that was all child's play compared to the amount of downright geeky detail he came up with for the **JLA/Avengers** crossover. Even after working three decades in the comics biz, I was humbled by Kurt's awesome ability to incorporate what could be a jumble of comics history, characters and, let's face it, out and out arcania and corral them all into a cohesive, crackerjack story. That's what made working with Kurt such a blast – he was always a servant to the story. He loves a good yarn and has the wordsmith chops to tell it well.

Among all the partners I've worked with in my career, my collaborations with Kurt stand among the best I've

Captain America fighting side-by-side with Bucky, the Sub-Mariner and the Invaders from Marvels #1.

The cover to one of the greatest crossover events of all time: *JLA/Avengers #1!*

ever encountered. Kurt is as generous as he is creative. Like the best partners, we inspired each other to give a little more with each new adventure, to up the amount of detail, both visual and conceptual, that we felt could add deeper layers to the story. Kurt's stories always had a sense of being part of a bigger picture, with little acorns of subplots scattered throughout that would sprout into major story oaks in upcoming issues.

Add to all that the friendship and respect that developed between Kurt and me during our times together and you might be able to understand why I hold him in such regard. I'm pretty well known for being friendly and gregarious when I meet the fans, and I'm happy to say that, whenever we appeared together at conventions and book signings, Kurt's wit and charm definitely gave me a run for my money. Moreover, his intelligence and memory, especially about comics both historic and current –– that darn eye for detail again – put me to utter shame. His enthusiasm and quick wit are infectious and it is evident in his work as well as in his persona.

I can only hope that Kurt and I will work together again someday. If not, I will always have the pride of knowing that I helped tell some great stories with him.

He also pronounces my last name correctly as well. Just another small detail.

George Pérez
2007

MARVEL
POWER MAN AND IRON FIST
©1983 MARVEL COMICS GROUP
60¢
98
OCT
02149
APPROVED BY THE COMICS CODE AUTHORITY
THEY AREN'T DEAD YET! BUT WHEN THEY HIT THE WATER...?

KURT BUSIEK STORY • ERNIE CHAN PENCILS • ANDY MUSHYNSKY INKS • JANICE CHIANG LETTERING • BOB SHAREN COLORING • DENNY O'NEIL EDITING • JIM SHOOTER OVERSEEING

CHRISTMAS-- IT IS THEM!
SHADES AND COMANCHE!
DON'T YOU TWO TURKEYS EVER GET TIRED 'A THIS? EVERY TIME YOU SHOW UP-- I GOTTA WASTE MY TIME POUNDING YOUR HEADS!
WHY DON'T YOU JUST SKIP IT, HUNH?
UH-UH, LUCAS-- THIS TIME IT'S GONNA BE DIFFERENT!
'CAUSE THIS TIME--
--WE ARE THE NEW AND IMPROVED SHADES AND COMANCHE!
DIG?
WHAMM!
SO YOU GOT YOURSELF A SUPER-POWER, HUNH? THAT REALLY TICKS ME OFF!
NOW IT'S GONNA TAKE ME LONGER TO WHIP YOUR TAILS--
--AND I HAVE ALREADY MADE PLANS FOR THE DAY!
SHOOT, SHADES-- OL' LUCAS AIN'T GOT THE PICTURE YET!
YOU GOIN' DOWN, BOY!
WHAT--YOU'RE GONNA TAKE ME OUT WITH AN ARROW?
IT AIN'T JUST "A ARROW," LUCAS--

--SEE?
THE IMPACT OF THE ARROW KNOCKS LUKE BACKWARD--
HUNH!
--AND THEN THE TIP BURSTS, COATING HIS CHEST WITH A POWERFUL ADHESIVE--STICKING HIM TO THE WALL!
JUST LIKE FLYPAPER, HUNH, SHADES?
AIN'T IT THE TRUTH?
NOW LET'S SHOW OUR OLD SEAGATE BUDDY--
--THAT AGAINST SHADES AND COMANCHE--
300 POUNDS A' STEEL-HARD SKIN AND MUSCLES AIN'T WORTH SQUAT!
THIS TIME THE ARROW HAS AN EXPLOSIVE TIP. IT COMBINES WITH SHADES' POWER BLAST--
--TO PRODUCE DEVASTATING RESULTS!
HOLY--!
THAT'S POWER MAN!
WELL, WHADDYA KNOW--HE'S STILL BREATHING!
IF HE WAKES UP, KIDS--JUST TELL HIM A COUPLE OF FRIENDS STOPPED BY TO SETTLE AN OLD SCORE.

MEANWHILE, WE FIND THE OTHER HALF OF OUR HEROIC DUO AT THE NEW SUBURBAN PLANT BUILT BY RAND-MEACHUM, INCORPORATED...
BOY! THINGS NEVER SLOW DOWN, DO THEY?
JUST AFTER I DECIDE TO TRY AND PICK UP THE PIECES OF MY LIFE AFTER BEING DISOWNED BY K'UN-LUN...
...I FIND A MYSTERIOUS MYSTIC GEM, WHICH MAY OR MAY NOT COME FROM THERE...
...AND THEN I'M ATTACKED BY FERA WHO DOES COME FROM K'UN-LUN-- AND SHE STEALS THE GEM!
I NEED SOMETHING DOWN-TO-EARTH AFTER ALL THAT...
...AND SINCE I AM MAJORITY STOCKHOLDER IN THIS CORPORATION...
...I MAY AS WELL STOP IN AND SEE MY MONEY AT WORK!
RAND & ACHUM
OH MY-- IT'S HIM!
M-MISTER RAND! HOW NICE TO SEE YOU!
UH, COULD YOU TELL ME WHERE JOY MEACHUM'S OFFICE IS? SINCE SHE MOVED TO THIS PLANT, I--
DANNY! WHAT A SURPRISE! LONG TIME NO SEE!
NOT SINCE YOU MADE ME PROXY HOLDER FOR YOUR STOCK.*
*WAY BACK IN #54.
HELLO, JOY. I WAS AT LOOSE ENDS, SO I FIGURED I'D STOP BY AND SEE HOW YOU WERE DOING WITH IT.
IT'S STILL HERE, SAFE FOR WHENEVER YOU WANT TO TAKE UP THE REINS AGAIN.
THAT MAY BE AWHILE--I STILL HAVEN'T GOTTEN TOTALLY USED TO BEING BACK ON EARTH... I'D PROBABLY RUIN THE COMPANY IN A WEEK!
OH, I'M SURE YOU WOULDN'T--CONSIDERING YOU'RE HELPING RUN HEROES FOR HIRE IN YOUR, UH, OTHER IDENTITY.
HERE, WHY DON'T I GIVE YOU A TOUR OF THE NEW FACILITY...

BUT JUST AS JOY MEACHUM IS NOT THE ONLY EXECUTIVE AT THIS COMPANY... THE SITUATION IS NOT ENTIRELY FRIENDLY FOR DANNY RAND HERE...
WHAT?!
IRON FIST-- HERE?
WHY DID HE OF ALL PEOPLE, HAVE TO SHOW UP HERE-- AND WHY NOW?
I DON'T NEED THIS!
EVERY TIME MY PLANS HAVE RUN AFOUL OF IRON FIST-- I'VE BEEN LUCKY TO ESCAPE JAIL!
SINCE HE APPEARED ON EARTH-- I'VE TRIED TO HAVE HIM KILLED-- AT THE ORDERS OF MASTERLORD!
BUT I'VE NEVER BEEN ABLE TO MANAGE IT! HE'S TOO GOOD!
LORD, I HOPE MASTERLORD WASN'T MONITORING ME JUST THEN!
IT'S EERIE THE WAY HE ALWAYS KNOWS WHAT I'M THINKING!
AND WHAT MAKES YOU SO NERVOUS,
GAH! IT'S HIM!
N-NOTHING, MASTERLORD, I--
SILENCE, MEACHUM! YOU WERE CONTEMPLATING WAYS TO PREVENT IRON FIST FROM DISCOVERING OUR PLANS.
YOU ARE A COWARD, MEACHUM! DO NOT TRY TO TRICK IRON FIST--KILL HIM! AND BRING ME HIS HEART!
Y-YES, MASTERLORD!
AM I GLAD THAT'S OVER! HE SCARES ME ALMOST AS MUCH AS IRON FIST!
IT'S A GOOD THING I ARRANGED FOR SPECIAL HELP AFTER IRON FIST GOT IN OUR WAY OVER THAT POWER GEM.
THEY'LL HAVE TO KILL HIM--IF THEY CAN!

NEARBY...
AND THIS IS OUR SHIPPING AREA, WHERE THE GOODS MANUFACTURED AT THIS PLANT ARE SENT OUT TO THE PURCHASERS.
HUNH? WHAT ARE THOSE DOING HERE?
SOMETHING WRONG, DANNY?
THESE ARE THE GUNS THAT THAT PRIVATE ARMY WAS CARRYING WHEN THEY TRIED TO STEAL THE GEM! THEY WERE WORKING WITH FERA!
NO--IT'S JUST THESE. THEY LOOK ODD.
SOME KIND OF TOY?
HA! SOME TOY! IT'S A NEW WEAPON WE MANUFACTURE FOR VARIOUS SECURITY FORCES, ACTUALLY.
HERE--WHY DON'T YOU KEEP THIS ONE AS A SAMPLE? MAYBE HEROES FOR HIRE COULD PLACE AN ORDER SOMEDAY.
AND, AFTER THE TOUR HAS BEEN CONCLUDED...
THIS GUN... IF IT MEANS WHAT I THINK IT COULD...!
SO LONG, DANNY--DON'T STAY AWAY SO LONG THIS TIME, OKAY?
MAYBE WE CAN MEET FOR LUNCH SOME TIME?
SURE--I'D LIKE THAT! SEE YOU LATER!
SHORTLY, UNAWARE OF HOW CLOSE IRON FIST HAS COME TO HIS SECRET...
OKAY, OKAY! I'LL GIVE YOU THE MONEY BEFOREHAND!
WE'LL SET UP A MEETING SOMETIME TODAY.
HM?
WHAT WAS THAT ABOUT, WARD?
OH, NOTHING, JOY. JUST NORMAL BUSINESS STUFF. WHY--DON'T YOU TRUST YOUR OLD UNCLE?
ABOUT AS MUCH AS I'D TRUST A SNAKE!
YOU'RE UP TO SOMETHING, UNCLE WARD...
...AND I WANT TO KNOW WHAT IT IS!

AN HOUR LATER, AT THE PARK AVENUE OFFICES OF HEROES FOR HIRE...
DANNY--CUT IT OUT!
I'M TENSE. I PRACTICE WHEN I'M TENSE.
YEAH, WELL--YOU'RE MAKIN' ME NERVOUS! I AIN'T USED TO TALKIN' TO PEOPLE WHEN THEY'RE THE WRONG WAY UP.'
I WANT TO INVESTIGATE WHAT'S HAPPENING AT RAND-MEACHUM.
THAT GUN COULD BE THE KEY TO WHAT'S GOING ON WITH MY MYSTIC GEM!
AND I STILL SAY NO WAY!
I'M GOIN' AFTER SHADES AND COMANCHE--AND IF YOU AIN'T COMIN' WITH ME--THEN I'LL GO IT ALONE!
BOYS, BOYS--THERE'S NO NEED TO SNAP AT EACH OTHER!
AFTER ALL, I MIGHT POINT OUT THAT YOU'RE NOT GETTING *PAID* FOR EITHER OF THESE ENDEAVORS!
STILL, I AM YOUR BUSINESS MANAGER--AN AS SUCH, WILL GIVE YOU THE BENEFIT OF MY ADVICE.
AS I SEE IT, YOUR PROBLEMS CAN BE SOLVED BY PUTTING A MODICUM OF PRACTICAL THOUGHT INTO THE SITUATION--
--AS WELL AS A LITTLE *DEVIOUSNESS*!

WHAT DO YOU MEAN, JERYN?
TOO MANY PEOPLE AT RAND-MEACHUM KNOW YOUR DOUBLE IDENTITY--JOY DOES, AND POSSIBLY WARD--FOR IRON FIST TO BE SEEN NOSING AROUND THERE...
BUT THAT SHOULDN'T STYMIE US...
...ALL WE NEED TO DO IS HIRE THE LOVELY LADIES AT NIGHTWING RESTORATIONS TO DO OUR SNOOPING FOR US!
B-BUT--THEY'RE MY FRIENDS! WE CAN'T JUST HAVE JENNIE CALL THEM UP--AND *HIRE* THEM! IT'S SO--IMPERSONAL!
FINE, DANIEL...
...THEN *YOU* TALK TO THEM!
A LITTLE MORE THAN HALF A PHONE CONVERSATION LATER...
THE THING IS, I KNOW BUSINESS HASN'T EXACTLY BEEN BOOMING AT OUR AGENCY--
--BUT I *STILL* DON'T WANT YOU CREATING *CHARITY WORK* FOR US!
"CHARITY WORK"? THIS WASN'T EVEN MY IDEA, MISTY!
AS A MATTER OF FACT, I'M AGAINST IT!
FERA'S INVOLVED IN THIS--IT COULD BE DANGEROUS!

WHAT?!
GIMME THAT PHONE, MISTY!
IF YOU'RE GOING TO BE THAT WAY ABOUT IT, DANNY--
--NIGHTWING RESTORATIONS IS IN!
I WOULDN'T QUITE PUT IT THE SAME WAY COLLEEN DID, DANNY--
--BUT IF YOU'RE STARTING TO GET OVER-PROTECTIVE AGAIN, THEN WE'D BETTER SHOW YOU WHAT WE'RE CAPABLE OF.
WE'LL TAKE THE CASE.
AND...
WELL DONE, M'BOY, WELL DONE! YOU HANDLED THAT LIKE A MASTER OF RHETORIC!
BUT... I MEANT IT! I'D RATHER THEY SAID NO!
AH WELL, CHIN UP-- RESULTS ARE WHAT COUNT, AFTER ALL.
LET'S CUT OUT THIS TALKIN', HUNH?
SHADES AND COMANCHE ARE OUT THERE SOMEWHERE-- AND I GOT ME SOME BRUISES THAT KEEP REMINDIN' ME A'THE FACT. I'M ITCHIN' TO GET EVEN!
OKAY, LUKE-- WE MIGHT AS WELL GO--
--NOW THAT I'VE GOT NOTHING BETTER TO DO.

SO...
...A LOT OF OTHER FILM STUDENTS THINK IT DOESN'T MATTER WHAT YOU'RE FILMING--JUST HOW YOU FILM IT.
UH-HUH.
ME, I THINK FRANK CAPRA HAD THE RIGHT IDEA--THE SUBJECT IS ALL-IMPORTANT AND IT'S UP TO THE DIRECTOR--
--HUNH?
C'MON, D.W. YOU WANT TO GET THAT DOCUMENTARY ON US SHOT, YOU BETTER TAG ALONG--
--YOU'RE GONNA GET TO SEE US STOMP SOME REAL TURKEYS!
AND, OUT ON THE STREET...
WELL, LUKE, WHAT NOW? AFTER ALL--THEY'RE YOUR ENEMIES.
OK--FIRST WE--
--AW NUTS! I FORGOT--
--I TOLD HARMONY I'D MEET HER FOR LUNCH HALF AN HOUR AGO!
AIN'T NO WAY I CAN GET OUTA THIS ONE--
--AND THERE AIN'T NO WAY D.W. CAN FILM IT, NEITHER!
I'LL CATCH YOU BOTH LATER!
RIGHT.
FOR THIS WE CAN'T INVESTIGATE RAND-MEACHUM?
WELL, AS LONG AS LUKE'S EATING--Y'WANT TO GRAB A PIZZA OR SOMETHING?

SHORTLY...
OKAY, SO I'M LATE. D'YOU STILL GOTTA GIVE ME THE COLD SHOULDER?
OH, LUKIE-- THAT ISN'T IT!
I'M JUST TRYING TO UNDERSTAND WHY YOU SUDDENLY CHANGED YOUR MIND ABOUT MOVING OUT OF THAT AWFUL TIMES SQUARE!
BUT THEN, MAYBE I SHOULD ASK THAT DR. CLAIRE TEMPLE ABOUT IT--
--I'M SURE SHE CAN OFFER SOME VERY PERSUASIVE REASONS!
AW C'MON, HARMONY-- THAT AIN'T FAIR!
I EXPLAINED IT TO YOU--I CAN'T GO OFF AND LEAVE ALL THOSE PEOPLE WHO DEPEND ON ME--
...BESIDES, I KINDA LIKE THE PLACE.
I'M SURE YOU EXPECT ME TO BELIEVE THAT...
BUT IT'S-- HEY, WHERE'RE YOU GOIN'?
OH, I'LL BE BACK-- I'M JUST GOING TO THE LADIES' ROOM.
I'M NOT MOVING OUT OR ANYTHING.
OH, THIS IS WORKING OUT JUST FINE! LUKIE IS RESPONDING BEAUTIFULLY!
WHEN I GET BACK, HE'LL BE PROPERLY APOLOGETIC--AND THEN THINGS WILL BE JUST PEACHY!
WHAT AM I DOIN' WRONG?
NOTHIN' I CAN SAY SEEMS TO PLEASE HER-- SHE SNAPS AT EVERYTHING...
I GOTTA PLAY MY CARDS RIGHT--GET BACK ON HER GOOD SIDE...

HOLD IT.
I DO NOT *BELIEVE* I WAS THINKIN' WHAT I WAS JUST THINKIN'!
I AIN'T *NEVER* BEEN THE TYPE TO CRAWL TO NO WOMAN!
HARMONY WANTS TO BE LIKE THAT--LET HER!
LET HER EAT ALONE, TOO!
Restaur
SHORTLY, AT THE GEM THEATER...
LOOK WHO'S BACK. HOW'D YOUR DATE GO, LUKE?
ROTTEN.
YOU THOUGHT I WAS MAD BEFORE--
--I GOT ME A MAD ON NOW THAT SHADES AN' COMANCHE'RE GONNA BE LUCKY IF THEY *LIVE* THROUGH!
LET'S HIT THE STREET.
SO...
I WOULDN'T THINK HARMONY COULD *GET* LUKE THAT MAD. I WONDER...
...IS SOMETHING DEEPER BOTHERING HIM?
SO AS I SAID BEFORE--HOW DO WE FIND THESE GUYS?
NO PROBLEM THERE, FIST. SHADES AND COMANCHE AIN'T THE TYPE TO DO MUCH HIDIN'!
ALL WE GOTTA DO...

...IS FOLLOW THE GRAPEVINE.
THEY WAS IN A JOINT ON 105TH-- SQUEAKY JACK AND SOME OTHER DUDES WERE NEAR 'EM.
THANKS, PIERRE.
THEY HAD A MEETIN' TO GO TO. SAMMY THE TAPPER WAS CLOSER--MAYBE HE HEARD WHERE.
YEAH, I HEARD... THEY WERE HEADED FOR A PARK--
--UP NEAR THE GEORGE WASHINGTON BRIDGE.
SURE ENOUGH...
--AND BRING ME HIS HEART!
IT'LL BE A PLEASURE, MEACHUM.
AND WITH THESE POWER-GIMMICKS YOU SET US UP WITH-- IT'LL BE A BREEZE!
DON'T UNDERESTIMATE IRON FIST. HE'S RESOURCEFUL.
YEAH, BUT WE WOULDN'T BE ABLE TO SPEND THIS IN JAIL-- SO WE'RE MOTIVATED.
BUT GOOD!
THEN...
THERE YOU ARE SUCKERS!
I WAS BEGINNIN' TO THINK YOU'D GONE HOME!
LUCAS! BOY, YOU JUST LOOK FOR TROUBLE, DON'T YOU?
HEY, THE HONKY'S HERE TOO! NOT BAD!
OH, NO!
WARD MEACHUM DUCKS INTO THE SHRUBBERY, AND...
I MOVED QUICKLY-- AND I WAS BEHIND THE OTHERS! I DON'T THINK HE GOT A LOOK AT MY FACE!
I HOPE HE DIDN'T.

DO ME A FAVOR, TURKEYS--
PUT UP A GOOD FIGHT. I DON'T WANT THIS TO END TOO QUICK!
HA! YOU WISH, LUCAS!
NOT ONLY DO WE GET PAID TO OFF YOUR PARTNER--
--BUT NOW WE GOT THE CHANCE TO BASH YOU AROUND SOME MORE, TOO!
A FEW YARDS AWAY...
HUNH? THAT KID-- HE'S GOT A CAMERA!
THAT--THAT MEANS HE MIGHT HAVE GOTTEN ME ON FILM--PAYING OFF TWO KNOWN FELONS!
WHY DOESN'T ANYTHING EVER GO RIGHT FOR ME?
RIGHT NOW, MY FIRST PRIORITY IS TO GET OUT OF HERE--
-- BUT I HAVE TO DO SOMETHING ABOUT THAT KID--AND SOON!
MEANWHILE...
YOU TAKE IRON FIST, SHADES--
--I GOT LUCAS!
HATE TO DISAPPOINT YOU, COMANCHE-- BUT I'M BRACED FOR YOU THIS TIME!
PHOOM!
OH, YOU ARE, HUH?
TELL ME, LUCAS...

--YOU BRACED FOR THIS?
HUNH?
BRAK!
UHHHHH!
HA! YOU GOT HIM GOOD, SHADES!
IN ANSWER, LUKE CAGE CLIMBS TO HIS FEET--
HOLY--!
YOU GOTTEN ANY TOUGHER SINCE THE LAST TIME WE MET, LUCAS?
MAYBE. BUT ONE THING'S FOR SURE--
--YOU'VE GOTTEN DUMBER!
HEY--THAT TRICK MIGHT NOT'A WORKED ON LUCAS--
--BUT IT OUGHTA DO A REAL NUMBER ON IRON FIST HERE!
FIRE AWAY, COMANCHE.

COMANCHE RELEASES HIS BOWSTRING--
--AND TWO EXPLOSIVE ARROWS FLY UNERRINGLY TO THEIR MARKS!
FOOM!
FOOM!
THE RUINED WALL SHUDDERS--ITS BASE CRUMBLES--
--AND IT BEGINS TO TOPPLE!
I DON'T GET IT!
HE'S NOT MOVIN'--JUST STANDIN' THERE--
--LETTIN' HIMSELF BE KILLED!
NOT QUITE, COMANCHE. WHAT HE'S DOING IS CONCENTRATING, SUMMONING HIS CHI--HIS IMMORTAL SPIRIT--AND CHANNELLING IT INTO HIS HAND...
...UNTIL THAT HAND BEGINS TO CRACKLE--TO GLOW--
SHKOW!
--UNTIL IT BECOMES LIKE UNTO--
--A THING OF IRON!

... AND WHEN THE DUST SETTLES...
... IRON FIST IS UNSCATHED.
WE SUPPOSED TO KILL THAT?!
NO WAY, JOSÉ!
SHADES! WHATTA WE DO NOW?!
HEAD FOR THE BRIDGE--IT'S HIGHER GROUND!
AND...
SO WHAT DO YOU THINK, FIST?
TURKEYS, RIGHT?
I'LL AGREE THEY'RE JERKS--BUT THEY'RE DANGEROUS JERKS!
MAYBE.
IF SO, IT'S A NEW DEVELOPMENT.
HERE--SLOW 'EM DOWN!
A DEFT FLIP OF THE WRIST, AND...
UHHHH!
THERE--THAT STOPS SHADES. AND THE WAY COMANCHE STICKS NEAR HIM FOR LEADERSHIP--
--WE SHOULD CATCH UP TO BOTH OF THEM.

OHHH... YOU NEARLY BUSTED MY LEG!
YOU'RE GONNA HURT FOR THAT!
I'M RIGHT HERE, SHADES.
WHAT'S STOPPING YOU?
BRAK!
OKAY, IRON FIST--EAT THIS!
UHH!
I WASN'T FAST ENOUGH!
IT'S ONLY A GLANCING BLOW, BUT--
THE IMPACT--IT SPUN ME AROUND--
--I'M FALLING INTO THE STREET!
NO! I CAN'T BRAKE IN TIME!
I'M GOING TO HIT HIM!!
IRON FIST DOESN'T HAVE TIME TO THINK ABOUT WHAT HE'S DOING...
...ONLY TO MOVE--WITH SPLIT-SECOND ACCURACY--AND IF HE MAKES THE SLIGHTEST MISTAKE...
...BUT HE DOESN'T. AND THUS, HE LIVES.

YOU IN IT DEEP NOW, LUCAS!
I GOT ME A WHOLE QUIVERFUL OF TRICK ARROWS--AND I AIN'T BARELY STARTED USIN' 'EM!
RIGHT.
AS THE ARROW HITS LUKE...
...A MASSIVE JOLT OF ELECTRICITY COURSES THROUGH HIS STEEL-HARD FRAME...
...LEAVING HIM SHAKEN, WOOZY, AND WEAK IN THE KNEES!
I DON'T BELIEVE IT!
THAT ARROW HAD ENOUGH POWER TO KILL A FULL-GROWN ELEPHANT!
C'MON, COMANCHE--DO I LOOK LIKE AN ELEPHANT?
STAY BACK, IRON FIST!
I DON'T KNOW HOW YOU KEEP DODGING ME--BUT SOONER OR LATER--I'LL GET YOU!
ACTUALLY, SHADES--DODGING YOUR BLASTS IS GETTING EASIER!
HE'S FIRING WITHOUT THINKING--AND THAT MAKES KEEPING OUT OF HIS WAY A SNAP!
COMANCHE! BACK TO BACK!
THAT WAY WE CAN HELP EACH OTHER OUT AND THEY WON'T BE ABLE TO GET NEAR US!
GREAT! I WAS HOPING THEY'D TRY SOMETHING LIKE THIS!
NOW IF ONLY LUKE KNOWS WHAT TO DO...

OKAY, JERKS-- YOU'VE HAD YOUR CHANCE!
NOW GIVE UP--OR I'M GONNA GET VIOLENT!
HOPE THEY FALL FOR A DUMB LINE LIKE THAT!
NOT A CHANCE, LUCAS!
I DON'T KNOW WHERE IRON FIST GOT TO, BUT ALONE--
--YOU DON'T STAND A CHANCE AGAINST OUR *TEAMWORK!*
WELL, WHAT DO YOU KNOW? IT WORKED!
YOU LOSERS ARE TOO MUCH, YOU KNOW THAT?
DON'T YOU KNOW THAT "BACK TO BACK" MEANS YOU WATCH OUT BEHIND EACH OTHER?
IF YOU'RE BOTH LOOKIN' IN THE SAME DIRECTION--
--SOMEONE CAN SNEAK UP BEHIND YOU!

LATER...
WE'LL BE BACK, LUCAS-- COUNT ON IT!
DON'T MAKE ME LAUGH, SHADES.
YOU TWO STARTED OUT AS TURKEYS-- AND YOU'RE GONNA STAY TURKEYS 'TIL THE DAY YOU DIE.
YOU'RE NO THREAT TO ME!
NO THREAT?
NO THREAT?!
IT'S ASTONISHING--VICTORY CAN BE IN YOUR GRASP--VICTORY CAN EVEN BE ACCOMPLISHED--
--AND IN ONE INSTANT--
LAUGH THIS ONE OFF, LUCAS!!
HIS VISOR-- IT STILL HAD POWER IN IT!!
--EVERYTHING CHANGES COMPLETELY!

YOU'RE GONNA WISH YOU'D NEVER DONE THAT, JACK! YOU'RE GONNA WISH YOU WERE NEVER BORN!
CAUSE NOW YOU'RE GOING UP FOR *MURDER!*
WELL, I'M GLAD! YOU HEAR ME? *I'M GLAD!*
I JUST KILLED POWER MAN AND IRON FIST!
NEXT ISSUE: SPLAT?

MARVEL®
POWER MAN AND IRON FIST®
©1983 MARVEL COMICS GROUP
TM
60¢
99
NOV
02149
APPROVED BY THE COMICS CODE AUTHORITY
MILGROM

Stan Lee PRESENTS: POWER MAN AND IRON FIST
"THIS DEADLY SECRET..."
A MOMENT AGO, EVERYTHING WAS FINE.
A MOMENT AGO, SHADES AND COMANCHE HAD BEEN DEFEATED, AND WERE BEING LED, CUFFED, TO THE PADDY WAGON.
THAT WAS A MOMENT AGO.
HA HA HA HA HA! DID YOU SEE THAT?! MY POWER-BLAST BLEW 'EM RIGHT OFF THE BRIDGE!!
KURT BUSIEK WRITER • ERNIE CHAN PENCILER • ANDY MUSHYNSKY INKER • JANICE CHIANG LETTERER • CHRISTIE SCHEELE COLORIST • DENNY O'NEIL EDITOR • JIM SHOOTER EDITOR-IN-CHIEF

AS CHOPPY GREY WATERS RUSH UP AT THE HEROES FOR HIRE...
QUICK, FIST! TRY TO GET RIGHT ABOVE ME--THAT WAY I'LL TAKE THE BRUNT OF THE IMPACT!
NO, LUKE--EVEN YOUR STEEL-HARD SKIN CAN'T TAKE THAT KIND OF SHOCK!
SO MAYBE I'M NOT GONNA LIVE THROUGH THIS--
--BUT ONE OF US IS GOING TO!
WHRAKKK!
FROM THAT HEIGHT, THE WATER IS LIKE IRON!
ALTHOUGH POWER-MAN ABSORBED MOST OF THE SHOCK, EVEN FOR IRON FIST, THE IMPACT IS BRUTAL.
HE FIGHTS FOR AIR--AND THERE IS NONE.
HE FIGHTS TO REMAIN CONSCIOUS--AND BARELY SUCCEEDS.
HE FIGHTS TO OPEN HIS EYES--
--AND HE SEES--
LUKE!
IS HE STILL ALIVE?
HE-HE'S SINKING SO FAST!
BLACKNESS STARTS CLOSING IN AS IRON FIST FORCES HIMSELF TO SWIM AFTER HIS PARTNER. IS IT JUST THE DIRTY RIVER WATER--
--OR ARE HIS OWN INJURIES TAKING THEIR TOLL?

MEANWHILE...
THEY'RE NOT COMING UP.
THEY'RE DEAD.
OKAY, YOU TWO-- IN THE WAGON. WITHOUT YOUR FANCY GIMMICKS, YOU'RE JUST ANOTHER PAIR OF PUNKS.
PUNKS WHO'RE GOING UP FOR MURDER!
HA! YOU THINK I CARE, COP? WHEN I'VE FINALLY DONE IT--FINALLY KILLED POWER MAN?
SHUT UP, PUNK-- YOU'RE STARTIN' TO MAKE ME SICK!
POLICE
DISPATCH, THIS IS 72 REPORTING IN
WE GOT BAD NEWS...
BACK AT THE BASE OF THE BRIDGE, THE SECONDS TICK SLOWLY BY...
THE BUBBLES SLOW... ALMOST STOP...
THEN...
AIR!!
GODS-- I NEVER KNEW SIMPLY BREATHING COULD FEEL SO GOOD!
I'VE GOT TO GET LUKE TO SHORE--HE'S SWALLOWED A LOT OF WATER.
I DON'T THINK HE'S BREATHING.

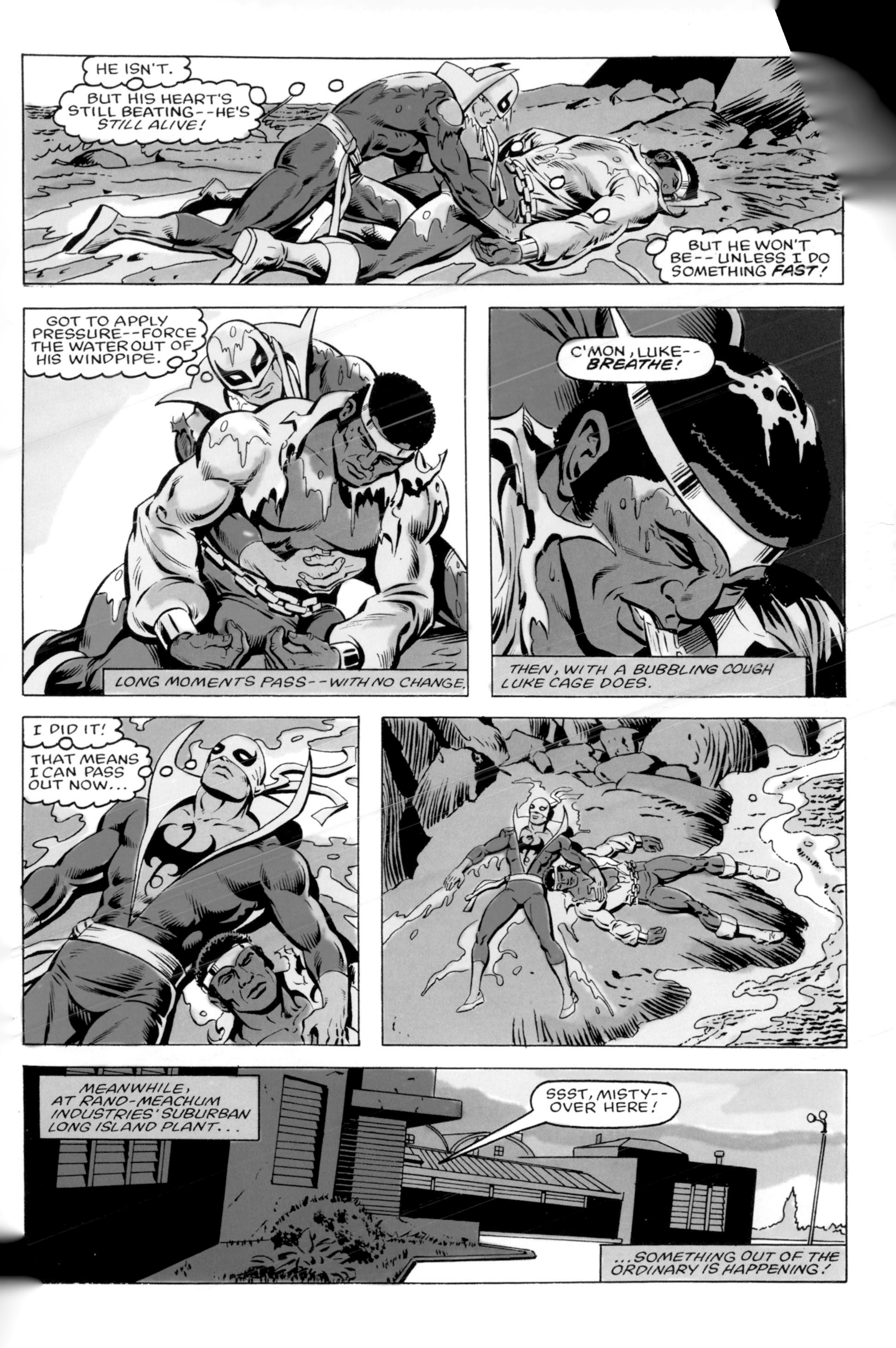
HE ISN'T.
BUT HIS HEART'S STILL BEATING--HE'S STILL ALIVE!
BUT HE WON'T BE--UNLESS I DO SOMETHING FAST!
GOT TO APPLY PRESSURE--FORCE THE WATER OUT OF HIS WINDPIPE.
LONG MOMENTS PASS--WITH NO CHANGE.
C'MON, LUKE--BREATHE!
THEN, WITH A BUBBLING COUGH LUKE CAGE DOES.
I DID IT!
THAT MEANS I CAN PASS OUT NOW...
MEANWHILE, AT RANO-MEACHUM INDUSTRIES' SUBURBAN LONG ISLAND PLANT...
SSST, MISTY--OVER HERE!
...SOMETHING OUT OF THE ORDINARY IS HAPPENING!

Y ARE COLLEEN WING AND
TY KNIGHT. . . TWO OF DANNY
ON FIST'' RAND'S CLOSEST
ENDS--AND TWO OF THE BEST
VESTIGATORS IN THE WORLD.
YUP--I THINK THOSE ARE OUR PIGEONS, ALL RIGHT.
THOSE ARE THE TURKEYS WHO BUSTED UP THAT HIGH-SOCIETY WEDDING A WHILE BACK--
--AND WHO ROBBED DANNY'S HOUSE TWO WEEKS AGO!
AND IF THESE ARE THEIR BARRACKS--THAT DEFINITELY LINKS BOTH ATTACKS TO RAND-MEACHUM!
GREAT--LET'S SEE WHAT ELSE WE CAN TURN UP.
AND IT'S NOT LONG BEFORE. . .
BINGO!
THERE'S THE GEM THEY STOLE FROM DANNY!
IT'D BE NICE TO SWIPE IT BACK. . . BUT WE'D BETTER NOT TRY.
THERE'S TOO MANY OF 'EM.
THE TWO MOVE ON, AND. . .
WHAT'S THAT?
I DON'T KNOW--BUT JUDGING FROM THE HONOR GUARD--IT'S IMPORTANT!
AND THE WAY THIS CAPER'S BEEN GOING--IT'S NOTHING GOOD!
YEAH. WELL, LET'S HEAD BACK AND REPORT WHAT WE GOT. IT OUGHT TO BE PLENTY!

WELL, THIS OUGHT TO SHOW LUKE AND DANNY! THEY WERE SO CONVINCED WE'D GET INTO TROUBLE-- THE WAY *THEY* ALWAYS DO--
ZZZAKK
HUNH?
WHAT WAS THAT?
IT'S--
--*EL AGUILA!*
KEEP YOUR DISTANCE, SEÑORS--
--YOU MAY HAVE ME OUT-NUMBERED, BUT AS LONG AS MY BIO-ELECTRIC BLASTS HOLD OUT--
--YOU WILL FIND IT VERY COSTLY TO KILL ME!
WHAT WAS THAT I WAS SAYING ABOUT NOT GETTING INTO A FIGHT?
OH, WELL...
...YOU CAN'T WIN THEM ALL!
AMIGAS! WHAT A WELCOME SIGHT!
HUNH?

GET THEM--
QUICK!
WE GOT ENOUGH PROBLEMS WITH THE GUY--WE DON'T NEED DAMES ON OUR BACK, TOO!
SORRY, GUYS--
--BUT IT'S NOT THAT EASY!
AGHK!
WHAT DOES THIS CHICK THINK SHE IS--A SAMURAI?
ACTUALLY, YES.
WELL, THIS DAME AIN'T PACKIN' A SWORD--AN' SHE AIN'T EVEN GONE FOR HER GUN!
THINK SHE'S POWER MAN, I BET!
NOT QUITE, JACK--
--BUT I'M CLOSE!
THANKS TO MY BIONIC ARM, ANYWAY.
SEÑORITA WING, YOU ARE A GOD-SEND! I OFFER HEARTFELT THANKS FOR SUCH TIMELY ASSISTANCE FROM TWO SO LOVELY!
AW, YOU LATIN DEVIL, YOU! BUT WHAT'S A NICE GUY LIKE YOU DOING IN A PLACE LIKE THIS?

THIS COMPANY'S OFFICIALS HAVE BEEN DOING A GREAT DEAL OF HIRING FROM THE CRIMINAL ELEMENT LATELY. NATURALLY, I INVESTIGATED--
--AND I SEEM TO HAVE DISCOVERED THEIR NEW EMPLOYEES.
I'LL SAY!
MEANWHILE, IN ANOTHER PART OF THE PLANT...
RRRRR
...SOMEONE IS ALERTED.
A VERY SPECIAL SOMEONE!
HER NAME IS FERA. SHE IS A WOLF IN HUMAN FORM. SHE WAS ASLEEP...
...AND SHE DOESN'T LIKE BEING AWAKENED!
BACK AT THE "DISTURBANCE"...
MANY THANKS FOR SEEING US TO THE DOOR, GENTLEMEN-- BUT I FEAR WE MUST TAKE OUR LEAVE!
NO NEED TO BOTHER ABOUT THE DOORMAN-- HE'S BEEN TIPPED!
COL, THAT WAS TERRIBLE. LET'S GET OUT OF HERE!
ZOT!
WHAK!
WHUD!
SUDDENLY...
HA! FERA HAS YOU, WOMAN!
FERA!
A QUICK NERVE PINCH, AND MISTY KNIGHT IS UNCONSCIOUS.
AT THAT, SHE'S LUCKY. FERA COULD HAVE EASILY SLIT HER THROAT.
THIS BLACK AND THE OTHER WOMAN WERE AT THE HOUSE OF DANIEL RAND! *
THEY ARE IN LEAGUE WITH IRON FIST!
*THEY MET IN #97--D.

THEN, THE ACTION SQUAD REGROUPS FOR AN ASSAULT...
OKAY, ZORRO--YOU AND YOUR LADY FRIEND'RE GOIN' DOWN!
THEY'VE CUT US OFF FROM MISTY! WE'LL HAVE TO CUT OUR WAY THROUGH THEM!
ALAS, SEÑORITA--I FEAR OUR BEST OPTION AT THIS POINT IS TO OBSERVE THE BETTER PART OF VALOR...
NO!
I WON'T RUN! NOT WITH MISTY PRISONER!
I REALIZE YOU ARE OVER-WROUGHT--
--BUT GETTING CAPTURED OR KILLED WILL NOT AID, MS. KNIGHT--
--WHILE GETTING HELP WILL!
BUT...SHE WOULDN'T LEAVE ME...MISTY...
AND...
A WISE DECISION, AMIGA!
IF YOU HAD INSISTED ON FIGHTING--I WOULD HAVE BEEN COMPELLED TO STAY, AND--
LOOK, AGUILA--DON'T PUSH IT, HUNH?
I REALIZE YOU WERE RIGHT--
--BUT I DON'T HAVE TO LIKE IT!
LET THEM GO. ONE PRIZE IS ENOUGH FOR THIS EVENING.
PUT THE BLACK IN WITH THE OTHER ONE.
"OTHER ONE"?

MEANWHILE...
OHH... I FEEL AS IF EVERY PART OF MY BODY IS BRUISED!
ME, TOO!
I'LL GET D.W. TO MAKE US A POT O'COFFEE.
YO! D.W.!
NO ANSWER. HE MUST BE--HEY!
THERE'S SOMEONE IN YOUR OFFICE!
THE HEROES FOR HIRE TENSE, READY FOR COMBAT...
...BUT WITH THE CLICK OF A LIGHT SWITCH...
RAFE! RAFE SCARFE!
MORNIN', LIEUTENANT. WHAT'S UP?
NICE TO SEE YOU TWO. ESPECIALLY AFTER I GOT A REPORT YOU WERE DEAD.
TROUBLE IS, THE TEAM THAT MADE THE REPORT NEVER GOT BACK TO THE STATION. BOTH MEN WERE KILLED, AND SHADES AND COMANCHE WERE SPRUNG...
I CAME BY TO SEE IF D.W. MIGHT HAVE ANY INFORMATION ON YOU TWO...
...AND I FOUND THIS!
HUNH? D.W.'S APARTMENT--IT'S BEEN TRASHED!
UH-HUH--AND NO SIGN OF D.W., EITHER!
LOOKS LIKE HE WAS KIDNAPPED!
EVEN MORE CURIOUS--HIS DARKROOM'S BEEN RANSACKED--
--AND THE REAL SENSELESS CLUE IS THIS--THE FILM RACK!
IT'S EMPTY! BUT WHY WOULD ANYONE STEAL D.W.'S FILM?

MEANWHILE...
FASTER, LIGHTNING, FASTER!
KPOW
WE MUST REACH ROSALIE'S BY NOON!
WHAT IS THIS?
I HAVE FERA SAVE YOUR WORTHLESS HIDES-- SEND YOU TO GET THE FILM THAT PUNK SHOT OF ME PAYING YOU OFF--AND WHAT DO YOU BRING ME? WESTERNS!
BUT WE TOOK ALL A' THE FILM!
EVEN THE ONE IN HIS CAMERA!
YOU HOPELESS IMBECILES-- IS THERE NOTHING YOU CAN DO RIGHT?
YOU DIDN'T EVEN BRING IRON FIST'S HEART WHEN YOU KILLED HIM!
HUNH?
I THOUGHT THAT WAS JUST AN EXPRESSION!
HA!
WHEN THE MASTER-LORD HEARS OF YOUR FOOLISHNESS--YOU SHALL LEARN JUST HOW EXPRESSIVE HE CAN GET!
IF YOU ACTUALLY SLEW IRON FIST--
--WHICH FERA DOUBTS!
IRON FIST--ALIVE? I HOPE NOT--BUT SOMEHOW I CAN'T BELIEVE SHADES AND COMANCHE EITHER!
FERA--PERHAPS YOU HAVE SOME CONSTRUCTIVE SUGGESTIONS TO OFFER?

SILENCE!
YOU HAVE NO AUTHORITY OVER FERA! HOLD YOUR TONGUE--OR SHE SHALL TEAR IT OUT!
FERA SHALL RETURN--WITH THE CORRECT FILM!
IF THESE TWO FOOLS COULD NOT FIND IT--IT IS PROBABLY IN PLAIN SIGHT!
UPPITY BROAD!
YOU SAID IT!
WHILE...
NO IDEA WHO COULD'VE KIDNAPPED AN UNASSUMING FILM STUDENT LIKE D.W.?
SHADES AND COMANCHE?
COULD BE--WE DON'T EVEN KNOW WHO THEY'RE WORKIN' FOR YET!
THEN...
COLLEEN! AN' THE EAGLE!
YOU'RE HERE!
WHAT'S HAPPENED? WHERE'S MISTY?
BUT BEFORE COLLEEN WING CAN SPEAK...
THAT'S EL AGUILA!
THERE'S MORE THAN A DOZEN WARRANTS OUT FOR HIM!
DIÓS MIO! I DON'T NEED THIS!

I'VE GOT TO TAKE THEM IN!
AND IF YOU TWO ARE ACCESSORIES IN ANY WAY...
IF YOU WISH, POLICEMAN--YOU MAY CHASE ME, AND I SHALL ELUDE YOU--
--AND ALL THAT SHALL BE ACCOMPLISHED IS THAT WE WILL BE DELAYED IN OUR EFFORTS TO RESCUE SENORITA KNIGHT!
ENOUGH!
WHAT? WHAT'S HAPPENED TO MISTY?!
BEFORE PATROLWOMAN MISTY KNIGHT LOST HER ARM, SHE WAS RAFAEL SCARFE'S PARTNER. THERE IS A BOND OF LOYALTY BETWEEN THEM--THAT WILL NOT BE SHATTERED BY ANYTHING SHORT OF DEATH.
IF POSSIBLE, THE BOND BETWEEN DANIEL RAND AND MISTY KNIGHT IS STRONGER--FOR THEIRS IS A BOND OF LOVE.
SHE--SHE'S STILL AT RAND-MEACHUM.
SHE WAS CAPTURED BY FERA.
I... I DIDN'T WANT TO LEAVE HER, BUT...
BY ALL THE GODS OF K'UN-LUN...
...I WILL SEE MISTY SAFE ONCE MORE--AND D.W., TOO...
...OR DIE TRYING!
THIS IS GETTIN' NUTSO!
OLD ENEMIES...NEW ONES...CREEPS WORKIN' FOR FIST'S COMPANY... MYSTIC DISCO BALLS... AND NOW OUR FRIENDS ARE DISAPPEARIN'!
WHEN IS THIS GONNA START MAKIN' SENSE?!

CRRASSSH!
WHA--?
HUNH?
EH?
FERA REJOICES AT SEEING YOU ALIVE, IRON FIST! NOW SHE MAY SLAY YOU HERSELF!
BUT FIRST TO BUSINESS! FERA HAS COME FOR THE FILM!
THIS IS GETTIN' WEIRDER!
IF YOU'VE HARMED A HAIR ON MISTY KNIGHT'S HEAD, FERA...
LET US BE PRAGMATIC, AMIGOS. THIS WOMAN KNOWS SOMETHING--
--SO THOUGH IT IS MOST UNGENTLEMANLY--
--WE MUST CAPTURE HER--
HRARRR!
--AND FORCE HER TO--AGH!

NOW YOU SHALL--EH?
HEY! LEAVE LOOSE A' HIM, FURRY!
SURE, HE MAY GET ANNOYIN' FROM TIME TO TIME, BUT THAT'S NO REASON TO...
YOU INTERCEDE FOR HIM?
THEN DIE IN HIS STEAD!
HEY-- WATCH THE MATERIAL, HUNH?
YOU GOT A LOT TO LEARN ABOUT POWER MAN AN' I'M GONNA TEACH YOU!
NOW HOLD STILL, AND I'LL...
HRAH! YOU HAVE A LOT TO LEARN ABOUT FERA AS WELL, BLACK!
BUT AS SHE LANDS...
WATCH IT, LADY! YOU MIGHT--
UH-OH! YOU DID TRIP!
ARRH! YOU'LL BLEED, FOR THAT, HUMAN!
I'M GOING TO ASK YOU SOMETHING, FERA --
--AND I'M ONLY GOING TO ASK YOU ONCE!

KRAK!
WHERE--
--IS--
THOK!
WHAK!
--MISTY--
--KNIGHT?!
I DIDN'T KNOW THE MAN COULD GET THAT MAD!
BUT...
NO MORE, IRON FIST!
YOUR SKILL IS INCREDIBLE--
SHE CAUGHT HIS ARM?
UHHHH!
--BUT FERA IS YOUR SUPERIOR!

OKAY, WOLF-LADY-- IT'S MY TURN.
YOU SEEM CALM, HUMAN--AS IF UNCONCERNED AT THE LOSS OF YOUR PARTNER.
WHAKT!
OH, I'M PLENTY CONCERNED!
BUT I WAS TAUGHT TO VIEW MY RAGE AS FUEL-- TO USE IT, NOT SHOW IT!
BUT...
YOU SHOULD HAVE STRUCK WITH NAKED STEEL, GIRL--
--BECAUSE WITH FERA--
--THERE ARE NO SECOND CHANCES!
--BLAAGKH!
FZAT!
--THOUGH IT GRIEVES MY HEART TO FIRE ON A WOMAN-- ESPECIALLY FROM BEHIND--
--THERE IS MUCH I WILL DO BEFORE I ALLOW YOU TO HARM COLLEEN WING!

YOU DIE FOR THAT ATTACK, SWORDSMAN--NOW!
DOES THAT MEAN YOU'RE LETTING ME GO?
HRNH?
FERA HESITATES, NOT KNOWING WHICH VICTIM TO SLAY FIRST!
THEN...
AND WITH THAT, FERA'S MIND IS MADE UP!
YOU, IRON FIST!
YOU ARE FERA'S PREY!
UH...
GET OFF A' HIM, FERA--
--NOW!
POW!
HRGH!
IN ALL HER YEARS, FERA HAS NEVER BEEN SO CONTINUALLY FRUSTRATED IN HER EFFORTS!
THE HUMAN SIDE IS GONE NOW--ONLY THE ANIMAL REMAINS.
KILL!
I'LL KILL YOU ALL!

BUT AS SHE CATCHES HER BREATH...
HERE WE ARE, FERA... COME AND GET US!
CHRISTMAS! AIN'T SHE EVEN BRUISED YET?
...SENSIBILITY RETURNS, AND WITH IT, REALIZATION.
SHE CANNOT FIGHT THESE FOES. THEY ARE TOO MANY FOR HER.
HEY! WHA--?
LIKE IT OR NOT--SHE MUST FLEE!
BLAM
BLAM
BLAM
OH, NO YOU DON'T!
THE ROAR OF THE AUTOMATIC FILLS THE ROOM...
...BUT WHEN THE LAST BULLET IS GONE...
SO MUCH FOR WEEKLY TARGET PRACTICE.
I MIGHT'VE HIT HER ONCE--BUT I DON'T THINK SO.
NOPE...
...IT LOOKS LIKE SHE'S MADE GOOD HER ESCAPE.
AGAIN.

AND WITH THAT REALIZATION, THE BATTLE TRULY ENDS. MUSCLES BEGIN TO UNTENSE, BREATHING BECOMES DEEPER AND MORE RELAXED, AND THE DAMAGE IS SURVEYED...
LOOK AT THIS PLACE!
IT'S A GOOD THING MY OFFICE IS SUCH A DUMP--OR ELSE I'D GO CRAZY TRYIN' TO REPAIR IT ALL THE TIME!
AS IT IS, WELL...
THAT SHOULD ABOUT DO IT UNTIL YOU CAN SEE A DOCTOR, AGUILA.
HOW DO YOU FEEL?
I SHALL RECOVER--
--BUT I FEAR IT WILL BE SOME TIME BEFORE I LOOK ON WOMEN SO KINDLY AGAIN.
PRESENT COMPANY EXCEPTED OF COURSE.
SHE SAID SHE WANTED A FILM--
--SO THEY DON'T HAVE THE ONE THEY'RE AFTER.
BUT ALL OF D.W.'S FILMS WERE TAKEN, WEREN'T THEY?
YEAH, THEY--
HOLD IT--I GOT AN IDEA.
I'LL BE BACK IN A MINUTE.
AND...
HE MUSTA BEEN WORKING ON THIS ONE LAST NIGHT--
--IT WAS STILL IN THE FILM DRYER, SO THE KIDNAPPERS MISSED IT!

SOON...
I THINK I KNOW HOW TO WORK THIS THING-- I'VE SEEN D.W. DO IT OFTEN ENOUGH...
WHAT COULD HE HAVE FILMED THAT'S SO IMPORTANT?
THAT'S US...
SO THIS IS PART 'A' THE DOCUMENTARY D.W.'S FILMIN' ON US.
THE FILM ROLLS ON...
SAY--THERE'S SHADES AND COMANCHE...
AND...HEY!
FREEZE THAT FRAME!
YOU FOUND IT, DANNY?
DID I?
THAT MAN IS WARD MEACHUM!
THAT MEANS...
...SHADES AND COMANCHE ARE WORKING FOR RAND-MEACHUM. AND THAT'S NOT ALL...
QUICKLY, COLLEEN TELLS THEM WHAT SHE AND MISTY OBSERVED EARLIER...
THEN...
SO WARD MEACHUM IS BEHIND EVERYTHING WE'VE BEEN THROUGH LATELY. OKAY.
I DON'T KNOW WHY HE'D BE INTERESTED IN MYSTIC GEMS--OR EVEN WORKING WITH FERA. BUT I DON'T CARE. HE KIDNAPPED MISTY KNIGHT--
...AND WE'RE GOING TO MAKE HIM PAY!

EPILOGUE:
IRON FIST IS BOTH RIGHT AND WRONG. WARD MEACHUM IS BEHIND ALL OF THE MACHINATIONS THAT HAVE RECENTLY BEEN PLAGUING OUR HEROES...
...BUT HE'S NOT DOING IT FOR HIMSELF.
THE TIME IS RIGHT! PLACE THE POWER-GEM ON THE PEDESTAL!
AS THE MYSTIC GEM TOUCHES THE PEDESTAL, IT BEGINS TO PULSE WITH ENERGY, EMANATING A SHRILL WHINE...
...AND DARKENING IN HUE TO AN UNEARTHLY BLOOD-RED!
AND AS ITS EERIE GLOW SUFFUSES THE ARCHWAY BEHIND IT, A SHIMMERING FIGURE APPEARS...
...IT COALESCES, HARDENS AND TAKES ON DEFINITION AS...
MASTER KHAN!
HOW ASTONISHING-- I'M ACTUALLY HERE.
IT'S MIRACULOUS THAT MY MINIONS MANAGED TO ACCOMPLISH AS MUCH AS THEY DID.
I'M HERE NOW-- AND I'LL DEAL WITH POWER MAN AND IRON FIST--
--PERSONALLY.
NEXT: POWER MAN AND IRON FIST #100! BE HERE!
the end.

MARVEL®
POWER MAN AND IRON FIST
TM
$1.00
100
DEC
02149
APPROVED BY THE COMICS CODE AUTHORITY
SPECIAL DOUBLE-SIZE ISSUE!
ERNIE CHAN 1983

THE CRYSTAL CLEARS...
AH--THERE YOU ARE!
YOU APPEAR CONCERNED-- COULD IT BE THAT YOU STILL HAVE NO INKLING THAT I AM THE FORCE BEHIND ALL OF YOUR TROUBLES?
Stan Lee PRESENTS:
SOUL GAMES!
A PITY THAT I CAN ONLY WATCH YOUR CONFUSED FACES, AND NOT HEAR YOUR QUERULOUS UTTERINGS...
...BUT NO MATTER--
--FOR SOON YOU SHALL BE DEAD, AND I SHALL HAVE BACK WHAT IS RIGHTFULLY MINE!
KURT BUSIEK WRITER • ERNIE CHAN PENCILER • MIKE MIGNOLA INKER • JANICE CHIANG LETTERER • CHRISTIE SCHEELE COLORIST • DENNY O'NEIL EDITOR • JIM SHOOTER EDITOR-IN-CHIEF

BELIEVE IT OR NOT, THIS IS A BUSINESS CONFERENCE, BETWEEN DANNY RAND, A.K.A. IRON FIST; LUKE CAGE, POWER MAN; AND JERYN HOGARTH; THE OWNERS OF HEROES FOR HIRE, INC.; AND THEIR SECRETARY, JENNIE ROYCE...
LISTEN TO ME, JERYN! D.W. AND MISTY HAVE BEEN KIDNAPPED-- MY HOUSE HAS BEEN ROBBED-- AND NOW WE KNOW THAT THE MAN BEHIND IT IS WARD MEACHUM!
THAT MEANS MISTY AND D.W. ARE PROBABLY BEING HELD AT HIS NEW PLANT! I WANT TO GO GET OUR FRIENDS BACK--
--AND I WANT TO GO NOW!
PLEASE, DANIEL--CALM YOUR VIOLENT TENDENCIES! REMEMBER, IN ANY ATTACK ON RAND-MEACHUM FACILITIES YOU'LL BE DESTROYING YOUR OWN PROPERTY--
--COSTING YOURSELF MONEY!
PERHAPS I COULD START MAKING INQUIRIES INTO MEACHUM'S AFFAIRS. BACKED BY YOUR VOTING STOCK, IT WOULD FORCE...
NO, JENNIE!
THIS ISN'T A BUSINESS DEAL! I CAN'T JUST SIT BY AND WATCH WHILE MY FRIENDS ARE IN DANGER!
I'VE GOT TO DO SOMETHING!
I'M WITH YOU, FIST! LET'S BLOW THIS CLAMBAKE AND GO GET THAT TURKEY!
BZZT!
HUNH? SOMEBODY AT THE DOOR--
GOT A PACKAGE HERE FOR "IRON FIST"--BUT THERE'S NO NO COMPANY HERE BY THAT NAME--ONLY YOU GUYS.
I'M IRON FIST. I'LL TAKE IT.

WHAT IS IT?
I DON'T KNOW. THERE'S NO RETURN ADDRESS...
HEART OF THE DRAGON!
IT'S MY GEM! THE ONE FERA STOLE!
BUT WHY WOULD ANYONE STEAL SOMETHING AND THEN JUST RETURN IT?
THE ANSWER COMES SWIFTLY, AS IRON FIST TOUCHES THE BLOOD-RED GEM...
...AND IT FLARES TO UNHOLY LIFE!
AAKGHHH!!
IRON FIST FEELS IT MYSTICALLY PROBING-- REACHING INSIDE HIS INNERMOST SELF...
...DRAWING OUT THE POWER OF SHAO-LAO THE UNDYING...
...DRAWING THAT WHICH GIVES HIM THE POWER OF THE IRON FIST...
...STEALING HIS VERY SOUL!
AND WHEN IT HAS FINISHED...
...OHHH...
...IT DEPARTS...
FIST--!
LOOKS LIKE HE'S IN SOME KINDA TRANCE--!

YOU ARE IRON FIST--AND YOU ARE REMEMBERING.
REMEMBERING YOURSELF, YOUR PARENTS, AND YOUR FATHER'S BUSINESS PARTNER, HAROLD MEACHUM, ON A QUEST TO FIND THE LEGENDARY CITY OF K'UN-LUN.
REMEMBERING THE LAST TIME YOU EVER SAW THOSE YOU LOVED...
...WHEN DISASTER STRUCK, AND YOUR FATHER'S LIFE DEPENDED ON HIS PARTNER...
HAROLD, FOR GOD'S SAKE--DO SOMETHING!
OH, I'LL DO SOMETHING ALL RIGHT, OLD FRIEND... BUT I DON'T THINK YOU'RE GOING TO LIKE IT!
...YOU LEARNED WHAT BETRAYAL MEANS.
REMEMBERING THE HORROR--THE KNOWLEDGE THAT YOU, TOO, WOULD DIE IN THE FROZEN HIMALAYAS.
BUT YOU DIDN'T.
AT LEAST, NOT BOTH OF YOU.
FOR ON THE THRESHOLD OF K'UN-LUN, YOUR MOTHER GAVE UP HER LIFE TO BUY YOU TIME...
...SO THE WOLFPACK WOULD CLAIM ONLY ONE VICTIM--NOT TWO.
INSIDE, LAD--QUICKLY!
YOU'D MADE IT TO K'UN-LUN. BUT YOU DIDN'T CARE. ALL YOU WANTED WAS REVENGE ON THE MAN THAT HAD CAUSED ALL THIS--REVENGE ON HAROLD MEACHUM.
THE NEXT YEARS WENT BY SWIFTLY, AS YOU BECAME THE STAR PUPIL OF LEI KUNG THE THUNDERER--AND YOU ACHIEVED MASTERY OF THE MARTIAL ARTS.
BUT THAT WAS NOT ENOUGH. YOUR THIRST FOR REVENGE DROVE YOU TO STRIVE FOR MORE.

AND YOU GOT IT-- WHEN YOU WON THE RIGHT TO FACE SHAO-LAO THE UNDYING-- A FOE WHO COULD NOT BE KILLED.
OR SO IT SEEMED-- UNTIL YOU STRUCK ON THE IDEA OF OF BLOCKING OFF THE SCAR THROUGH WHICH THE DRAGON'S HEART HAD BEEN TAKEN-- DENYING IT ITS LIFE-ENERGIES...
...AND THE UNDYING DIED-- LEAVING YOU INDELIBLY MARKED WITH A REMINDER OF THE VICTORY.
BUT MORE THAN THAT, IT GAVE YOU...
...THE POWER OF SHAO-LAO.
IT TRULY MADE YOU THE IRON FIST.
AND THAT WAS THE TIME TO LEAVE K'UN-LUN AND SEEK YOUR REVENGE.
WHEN YOU REACHED HAROLD MEACHUM, YOU LEARNED THAT SOMEONE ELSE KILLED HIM--
--AND HIS DAUGHTER ACCUSED YOU OF THE MURDER!
THOUGH YOU EVENTUALLY DEFUSED JOY MEACHUM'S BURNING HATRED-- YOUR PATH HAS SINCE LED YOU ACROSS THE PATHS OF MANY OTHERS.
FRIENDS... ENEMIES... PARTNERS. ALL HAVE ADDED SOMETHING TO THE UNDERSTANDING YOU SEEK OF YOUR NATIVE WORLD.
YOU ARE IRON FIST-- AND YOU ARE...

--AWAKE!
HUNH?
WHERE AM I?
AT CITY HOSPITAL, IRON FIST, AND NOT IN PARTICULARLY GOOD SHAPE, I'M AFRAID.
I CAN'T FIND ANYTHING PHYSICALLY WRONG WITH HIM, LUKE--
--BUT HE'S LOSING ENERGY, AT SOMETHING LESS THAN A CELLULAR LEVEL!
AND AT THE RATE IT'S DROPPING, IF THE PROCESS ISN'T STOPPED--
--HE'LL BE DEAD IN 24 HOURS!
I'LL TELL YOU WHAT'S WRONG, DR. TEMPLE. IT'S MY SOUL--IT'S GONE.
THERE'S NOTHING MEDICAL SCIENCE CAN DO FOR ME--
--UNLESS WE GET IT BACK!
HEY, HOLD ON, FIST! YOU AIN'T WELL! YOU CAN'T--
GODS!
KNEES... WEAK... CAN'T EVEN STAND...
TAKE IT EASY, FIST. WE'LL GET YOUR SOUL BACK.
WE WILL? CHRISTMAS--I DON'T EVEN KNOW WHAT I'M TALKING ABOUT! THIS STUFF IS WAY OUT'A MY LEAGUE!

LATER, IN THE HOSPITAL LOBBY...
SO YOU ARE HERE, LUKE!
H'LO, BOYS.
AFTERNOON, TOBY.
HIYA, HARMONY-- WHAT'S ON YOUR MIND?
WHAT WAS ON HARMONY YOUNG'S MIND WAS TO GIVE CAGE A PIECE OF IT--FOR SEEING HIS OLD FLAME CLAIRE TEMPLE AGAIN.
BUT ONE LOOK AT IRON FIST'S PALLID FACE, AND THE WHEELCHAIR...
...AND...
OH, LUKE-- IS SOMETHING WRONG?
THE UNDER-STATEMENT OF THE CENTURY, BABE.
THERE HAS BEEN A GREAT DEAL OF FRICTION BETWEEN THESE TWO OVER THE LAST FEW WEEKS --
-- BUT AT LEAST FOR THE MOMENT--IT'S GONE.
WHATEVER IT IS, LUKE-- COME BACK SAFE, HUH?
IF ANY HARM SHOULD COME TO YOU...
MAYBE OL' TOBY CAN HELP ON THAT SCORE. I BEEN HEARIN' ABOUT YOUR TROUBLES WITH THAT WARD MEACHUM.
YEAH, TOBY--AN' I CAN'T FIGURE IT! MEACHUM'S AN INDUSTRIAL CROOK--STEALIN' SOULS IS OUTA HIS LINE!
WELL, LUCAS... WORD IS THAT MEACHUM'S GOT HISSELF A BOSS-- AN' IT'S HIM CALLIN' THE SHOTS.
IRON FIST SPEAKS, HIS VOICE IS AS FLAT AND LIFELESS AS THE GRAVE...
YOU'RE RIGHT, TOBY.
AND I THINK I KNOW WHO IT IS...

MASTER KHAN!
AHH... I SENSE THE POWER RETURNING EVEN NOW...

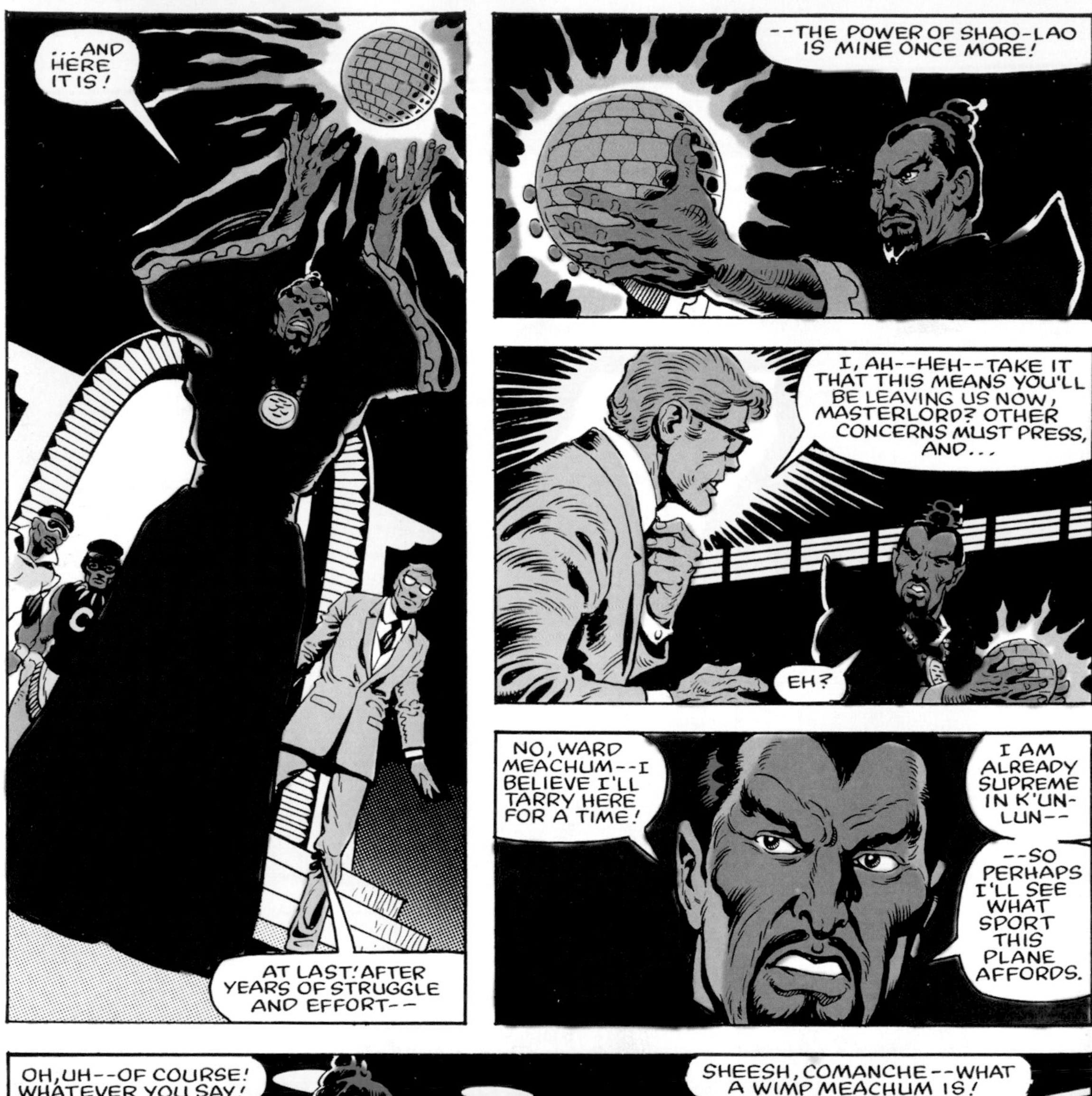
...AND HERE IT IS!
AT LAST! AFTER YEARS OF STRUGGLE AND EFFORT--
--THE POWER OF SHAO-LAO IS MINE ONCE MORE!
I, AH--HEH--TAKE IT THAT THIS MEANS YOU'LL BE LEAVING US NOW, MASTERLORD? OTHER CONCERNS MUST PRESS, AND...
EH?
NO, WARD MEACHUM--I BELIEVE I'LL TARRY HERE FOR A TIME!
I AM ALREADY SUPREME IN K'UN-LUN--
--SO PERHAPS I'LL SEE WHAT SPORT THIS PLANE AFFORDS.

OH, UH--OF COURSE! WHATEVER YOU SAY!
SHEESH, COMANCHE--WHAT A WIMP MEACHUM IS!
YOU SAID IT, SHADES!

MAYBE THE TWO OF US'D BE BETTER OFF TO DITCH MEACHUM AN' WORK DIRECT FOR KHAN.
HE MAY BE WEIRD, BUT HE GOT BRASS!
I LIKE THE WAY YOU'RE THINKIN', PARTNER!
FOOLS!
WHA--?
OH, GREAT--IT'S THE WOLF-LADY AGAIN!
YOU SHOULD REJOICE THAT YOU ANSWER TO SUCH A SPINELESS QUISLING AS MEACHUM!
YOU DO NOT WISH TO LEARN AS FERA HAS--THAT KHAN IS A HARSHER MASTER THAN ANY YOU WILL EVER KNOW!
UH, RIGHT.
MEANWHILE, IN A PART OF THE MANUFACTURING PLANT NOT ON THE ARCHITECT'S ORIGINAL PLANS...
THIS ISN'T SUPPOSED TO BE HAPPENING TO ME!
THIS IS THE SORT OF THING LUKE AND DANNY ARE USED TO! ME, I'M JUST A FILM STUDENT!
IF MISTY WOULD WAKE UP--HER BIONIC ARM COULD HAVE US OUTA HERE LIKE A SHOT!
MISTY! HEY, MISTY!
NO GO. SHE'S STILL OUT.
OH WELL--AT LEAST SHE'S STILL ALIVE.
AT LEAST WE BOTH ARE.

BACK IN MANHATTAN, AT POWER MAN'S OFFICE ABOVE 42ND STREET'S GEM THEATER, THE HEROES FOR HIRE HAVE CALLED IN SOME OUTSIDE HELP.
SO YOU SEE, THE FACTS ARE PRETTY SIMPLE--
GEM
THEATER
TEN
SHOWDO
GOING CLOCKWISE, THEY ARE: LIEUTENANT RAFAEL SCARFE, N.Y.P.D.; EL AGUILA, OUTLAW ADVENTURER; BOB DIAMOND, MARTIAL ARTS EXPERT; AND COLLEEN WING, SAMURAI.
--UNLESS THEY'VE MOVED--AND THEY HAVE NO REASON TO DO SO--WE KNOW WHERE D.W., MISTY, AND MY SOUL ARE BEING KEPT.
ALL WE HAVE TO DO IS GO GET THEM.
HOW CAN HE BE SO CLINICAL?
MAYBE IT'D BE BETTER IF RAFE DIDN'T COME. THIS IS OUT OF HIS JURISDICTION, AND IT MIGHT CAUSE HIM TROUBLE...
WHAT?!
MISTY KNIGHT WAS MY PARTNER, IRON FIST! IF SHE'S IN TROUBLE, I WILL HELP--JURISDICTION OR NO!
HAVE YOU NO HEART?
THAT'S EXACTLY RIGHT, RAFE. I HAVE NO HEART AT THE MOMENT.
IF YOU ARE COMING, YOU'D BETTER TAKE THIS. IT CAN BE SET ON STUN, UNLIKE YOUR REVOLVER. THAT WAY, YOU CAN'T GET IN TROUBLE FOR KILLING ANYONE.
AH...OF COURSE. THANK YOU.

CHRISTMAS-- THIS AIN'T THE FIST I KNOW!
HE'S MORE LIKE A ROBOT THAN A MAN!
HE CAN'T DIE-- HE JUST CAN'T! IF NOT FOR HIM--I'D BE NOTHIN' RIGHT NOW--NOTHIN'!
AND POWER MAN, TOO... REMEMBERS.
HE REMEMBERS BEING YOUNG AND FREE--AND IN LOVE.
INN
NITECLUB
REVA CONNORS WAS A FINE LADY. TROUBLE WAS...
... AN "OLD FRIEND" OF LUCAS' THOUGHT SO TOO--AND HE WANTED HER.
AND SO...
HUNH? WHAT IS THIS?
HEROIN, BOY. THAT'S BAD NEWS-- FOR YOU.
IT WAS A FRAME, OF COURSE--BUT THAT DIDN'T MATTER. LUCAS FOUND OUT WHAT JAIL WAS LIKE...
...AND WHAT HOPELESSNESS WAS.
BECAUSE THIS WAS SEAGATE--AND FOR A MAN LIKE LUCAS...
...IT WAS HELL!
AGAIN, QUIRT! BOY'S GOTTA LEARN TO SHOW RESPECT FOR HIS BETTERS.
RIGHT, CAP'N RACKHAM!
YOU GONNA CRAWL, BOY!
BUT LUCAS DIDN'T CRAWL, AND THAT MEANT...

... MORE BEATINGS, AND SOLITARY, AND WORSE -- UNTIL NOAH BURSTEIN CAME, WITH AN OFFER--
PAROLE.
YEAH? WHO DO I GOTTA KILL?
DR. BURSTEIN WAS LOOKING FOR A VOLUNTEER-- FOR AN EXPERIMENT IN CELLULAR REGENERATION. TO LUCAS IT MEANT ONLY ONE THING...
IF SITTIN' IN THIS THING IS GONNA GET ME OUTTA THIS JOINT, DOC--I DON'T CARE IF YOUR NAME'S FRANKENSTEIN!
BUT...
YOU AIN'T GETTIN' AWAY THAT EASY, BOY!
HEY-- NO!
BURSTEIN!
THE DOC AIN'T HERE, BOY! AND WHILE HE'S GONE--YOU'RE GONNA FRY!
RACKHAM-- NO! LET ME OUT!
I'M BURNIN' UP IN HERE--I'M BURNIN' UP!
BUT THE OVERLOADING MACHINE WAS NOT ONLY BURNING LUCAS--IT WAS CHANGING HIS BASIC CELLULAR STRUCTURE!
AND WHEN THE MACHINE BLEW... LUCAS WAS FOREVER DIFFERENT.
HE WEIGHED 300 POUNDS.
HE HAD SKIN LIKE STEEL.
AND MORE IMPORTANTLY...
HE HAD THE STRENGTH TO SHATTER CONCRETE!
I'M FREE! I'M FREE!
AND I'M NEVER GOIN' BACK! NEVER!

ON THE TRIP BACK TO NEW YORK, A CHANCE ENCOUNTER LED LUCAS TO REALIZE--
--THAT IF HIS NEWFOUND POWERS COULD GET HIM OUT OF JAIL--MAYBE THOSE POWERS COULD KEEP HIM OUT OF JAIL.
A NEW NAME--A COSTUME--AND HE BECAME...
LUKE CAGE HERO FOR HIRE
AND FROM THEN ON, THINGS WERE GONNA BE GOOD.
BUT THEY WEREN'T. THERE WAS ALWAYS TROUBLE--
--AND ALWAYS HIS PAST--
--COMING BACK AT HIM.
HE THOUGHT HE COULD STAY ONE STEP AHEAD OF IT, BUT IN THE END HE WAS CAUGHT--
--BY A MOBSTER NAMED JOHN BUSHMASTER.
IF HE WANTED HIS FRIENDS TO LIVE--HE'D DANCE TO BUSHMASTER'S TUNE. AND JUST LIKE THAT, THE HELPLESSNESS CAME BACK.
BUT THEN, CAGE MET IRON FIST, WHO OFFERED HIM A CHANCE TO FIGHT BACK--AND WHO HELPED HIM DO IT.
TOGETHER, THEY WON.
AND NOT ONLY THAT...
WITH THE EVIDENCE YOU'VE UNCOVERED, IT'S CLEAR TO THIS COURT THAT YOU SHOULD BE EXONERATED OF ALL CHARGES.
YOU'RE FREE TO GO, MR. CAGE.
FREEDOM--FINALLY!

AN' IF NOT FOR FIST--I'D BE IN JAIL AGAIN--OR DEAD--OR WORSE.
I CAN'T LET HIM DIE! I JUST CAN'T!
I GOTTA DO SOMETHING!
HEY, FIST--YOU SOUND LIKE YOU DON'T REALLY WANT TO GET KHAN!
SO WHY DON'T WE JUST CALL THE WHOLE THING OFF, HUNH?
LUKE! WHAT ARE YOU SAYING?
ARE YOU CRAZY?
I APPRECIATE WHAT YOU'RE TRYING TO DO, LUKE--
--BUT IT'S NOT WORKING. IT'S PART OF NOT HAVING A SOUL--
--I CAN THINK--INTELLECTUALIZE MY HATE TOWARD KHAN AND MY LOVE FOR MISTY.
--BUT I CAN'T FEEL ANYTHING.
UH-OH.
I WAS COUNTIN' ON YOUR FIGHTIN' SPIRIT TO GET US THROUGH THIS ONE.
BUT IF YOU AIN'T GOT IT--I'M GONNA HAVE TO DO IT FOR YOU.
LUKE CAGE IS GONNA TAKE ON YOUR FIGHT, FIST--
--AND I'M GONNA WIN IT!

RAND-MEACHUM INDUSTRIES, LONG ISLAND.
SHADOWS LENGTHEN AND NIGHT FALLS. ALL THE ORDINARY EMPLOYEES HAVE GONE HOME FOR THE DAY.
BUT AS TWILIGHT TRULY TAKES HOLD-- VISITORS ARRIVE.
OKAY--WE BEEN GOIN' OVER BLUEPRINTS A'THIS PLACE ALL DAY.
WE OUGHTTA HAVE IT DOWN BY NOW.
BUT AS THE GROUP TENSES, ABOUT TO MOVE FORWARD...
I... FEEL STRANGE...
DANNY! YOU'RE STANDING!
I... CAN SENSE MY SOUL IN THERE. IT'S CLOSE--
--AND I CAN DRAW ON IT A LITTLE... DRAW STRENGTH FROM IT...
AND... MISTY'S IN THERE, TOO
THERE'S ONLY A SMALL CATCH TO HIS VOICE--BUT IT'S REAL.
GREAT, FIST-- JUST GREAT.
BUT YOU BETTER SIT BACK DOWN-- SAVE IT FOR WHEN IT'S NEEDED.

YOU THREE GO IN THAT WAY--IT OUGHTTA BE EASIER TO SLIP PAST THE GUARDS THERE.
WE KNOW OUR PART, LUKE--HOW 'BOUT YOU?
SURE. ME 'N' RAFE 'N' THE ILLEGAL EAGLE--
--ARE GONNA TAKE THE DIRECT ROUTE!
HEY! WHA--?
WELL, LOOKA HERE--IT'S THE MARCHING BAND O'DOOM. REHEARSING FOR THE BIG PARADE, GUYS?
UH-OH.

MEANWHILE, NOT UNEXPECTEDLY...
BLLRRRRING!
IT'S NOT THE ALARMS THAT ARE IMPORTANT, SO MUCH...
...AS THE EFFECT!
HUNH? WHUZZAT? SHUT IT OFF!
GREAT. YOU'RE FINALLY AWAKE!
PEACHY. WHERE AM I?
NO, FORGET IT. I REMEMBER. THEY GOT YOU TOO, HUH? WHY?
WHO CARES? LET'S JUST GET OUT OF HERE!
IF YOU'RE SUGGESTING I USE MY HIDDEN TALENTS, D.W.--
SKREEEEKKH!
--CONSIDER IT DONE!
OKAY, WE'RE OUT.
YEAH, BUT THE GUARDS MUST'VE HEARD THAT RACKET, SO WHAT NOW?
WE BREAK HEADS, I GUESS. C'MON!

NO GUARDS. WHATEVER THE ALARMS ARE FOR--IT MUST BE PRETTY IMPORTANT TO CALL EVERYONE AWAY.
WAIT A MINUTE. MAYBE--
--YEAH! MY CAMERA!
I'M A LITTLE MORE CONCERNED WITH WHAT THOSE ALARMS ARE ABOUT.
WELL, THEY'RE MOSTLY ABOUT...
WHUFFF!
THAT'S TWO DOWN!
NICE WORK, COL! BUT FOR EVERY CREEP WE TAKE OUT--TWO MORE SHOW UP!
THIS ISN'T GETTING IRON FIST ANY CLOSER TO THE GEM!

WE GOTTA QUIT MESSIN' AROUND AN' KILL THE GUY IN THE CHAIR!
NOT AS LONG AS WE'RE HERE TO PROTECT HIM, TURKEY!
OW!
HA! I DID IT!
YOU READY TO DIE, IRON FIST?

NO.
WHRAKK!
HUNH?
WHAT?
THE CRIP GOT UP?
HE WAS FAKIN'!
WELL, NOT EXACTLY.
WAY TO GO, IRON FIST!
YOU EVEN *SOUND* ALMOST LIKE YOURSELF AGAIN!

SHE'S RIGHT--AS I GET CLOSER TO MY SOUL, I CAN DRAW MORE ENERGY FROM IT!

WHILE--
COME ON, ALREADY--THIS IS GETTIN' RIDICULOUS!
WE FOUGHT OUR WAY ALL THE WAY INTO THE ACTION SQUAD'S CENTRAL HQ--AND WE AIN'T RUN OUT OF 'EM YET!
WHAT'S MEACHUM GOT--A *CLONING MACHINE*?

BUT ALL THINGS MUST COME TO AN END, AND...
THAT'S ALL OF 'EM
HUNH?
SQUAD CENTRAL--COME IN! IRON FIST'S MOPPING THE FLOOR WITH US!
WE NEED HELP!
UH-OH. THAT MEANS THEY'VE BEEN DISCOVERED.
OH, WELL--THEY GOT AS FAR THEY COULD--
--LET'S SEE IF I CAN GET 'EM A LITTLE FURTHER!
OKAY, I'M HERE-- TALK TO ME.
GIVE ME YOUR LOCATION, AND WE'LL BE RIGHT THERE.
AND SO, IN MOMENTS...
SUCKER!
WISH EVERYTHING WAS THAT SMOOTH.
PERDONA ME, MI COMPADRE,--BUT MY POLICEMAN FRIEND HERE WISHES TO GO IN SEARCH OF MS. KNIGHT.
PERHAPS I SHOULD ACCOMPANY HIM RATHER THAN YOU, NO?
YEAH, THAT MAKES SENSE.
CELL BLOCKS'RE THAT WAY. I'M GONNA GO FIND FIST.

TOUCHDOWN!
WHAT?
YOU DID IT, LUKE!
YOU'VE GIVEN ME THE CHANCE TO RECLAIM...
...WHAT IS...
GO FOR IT, FIST!
...MINE!

MAR

The power gem of Quan is no more.
Without it, the power of Shao-Lao is free...
...and Iron Fist is whole once more.

The power gem of Quan is no more.
Without it, the forces that brought Master Khan to Earth do not exist...
...and the ages-old sorcerer is gone.

EPILOGUE:
I TELL YOU, YOU'VE GOT THE WRONG MAN! I WAS HERE WORKING LATE--THAT'S ALL!
HA! SOUNDS GOOD TO ME!
C'MON, EVERYBODY--LET'S
SQUARE FOR PIZZA, I

"It is with considerable difficulty that I remember the original era of my being..."

– *Mary Shelley*
Frankenstein

HORTON.
PHINEAS THOMAS HORTON.
QUITE POSSIBLY THE GREATEST SCIENTIST OF HIS TIME.
HE WAS MY FATHER.

HIS DISCOVERIES FAR OUTNUMBERED THOSE OF HIS CONTEMPORARIES.

YEARS AHEAD OF HIS TIME, HORTON'S ADVANCED KNOWLEDGE OF STEEL AND SYNTHETICS, COUPLED WITH A GREATER UNDER-STANDING OF THE HUMAN MIND, MADE HIM THE ENVY AND ODDITY OF THE SCIENTIFIC COMMUNITY.

FOR HIM, SCIENCE WAS THE MEANS BY WHICH HE COULD ACHIEVE HIS GOAL – TO UNLOCK THE DEEPER SECRETS OF CREATION ITSELF.

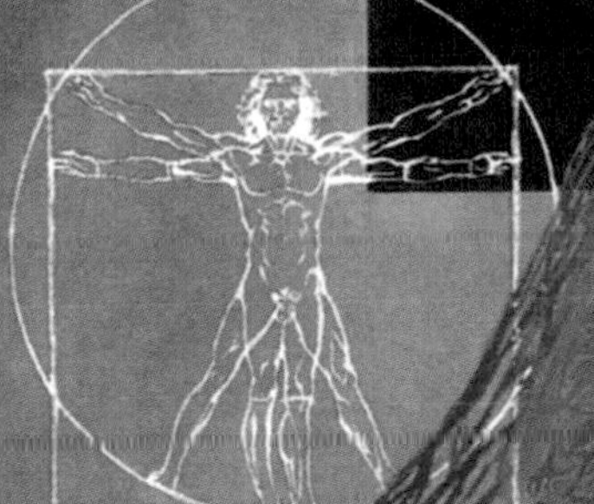

AS HE WITHSTOOD THE SKEPTICISM AND JEERS OF HIS COLLEAGUES, HE POOLED HIS RESOURCES TOWARD THE REALIZATION OF HIS GOAL.

THE STRESS OF HIS LIFE'S WORK WOULD CULMINATE IN ME.

I COULD BARELY COMPREHEND WHAT HAD HAPPENED TO ME IN THE COURSE OF MY SHORT LIFE.

I HAD BEEN RIPPED FROM MY ORIGINAL WOMB AND THRUST INTO A WORLD WHERE EVERY NOISE WAS EQUAL TO A SCREAM.

I HAD GONE FROM THE SECURITY OF DARKNESS TO A PLACE WHERE LIGHT BLAZED FROM EVERY DIRECTION.

AND YET, AS I BECAME AWARE OF THESE SENSATIONS...

...AS MY EYES,. MY EARS, AND MY SKIN WOULD FOCUS UPON THESE...

...THEY DISAPPEARED.

AND I ONCE AGAIN WOULD FALL BACK INTO THE DARKNESS AND SILENCE WHICH LACKED THE COMFORT THEY ONCE HELD.

THEY WERE NOW ONLY MOCKING REMINDERS OF ALL THAT WAS DENIED ME.

MY FATHER BROUGHT ME INTO THIS WORLD AND KEPT ME ALIVE WHEN OTHERS WOULD HAVE ME DESTROYED.

WHY, THEN, DID HE ALLOW ME THIS TORMENT? WAS HE SO EASILY WILLING TO FORSAKE ME?

WAS IT POSSIBLE THAT, WHILE I BELIEVED IN HIM AS A FATHER...

...HE DID NOT BELIEVE IN ME AS A SON?

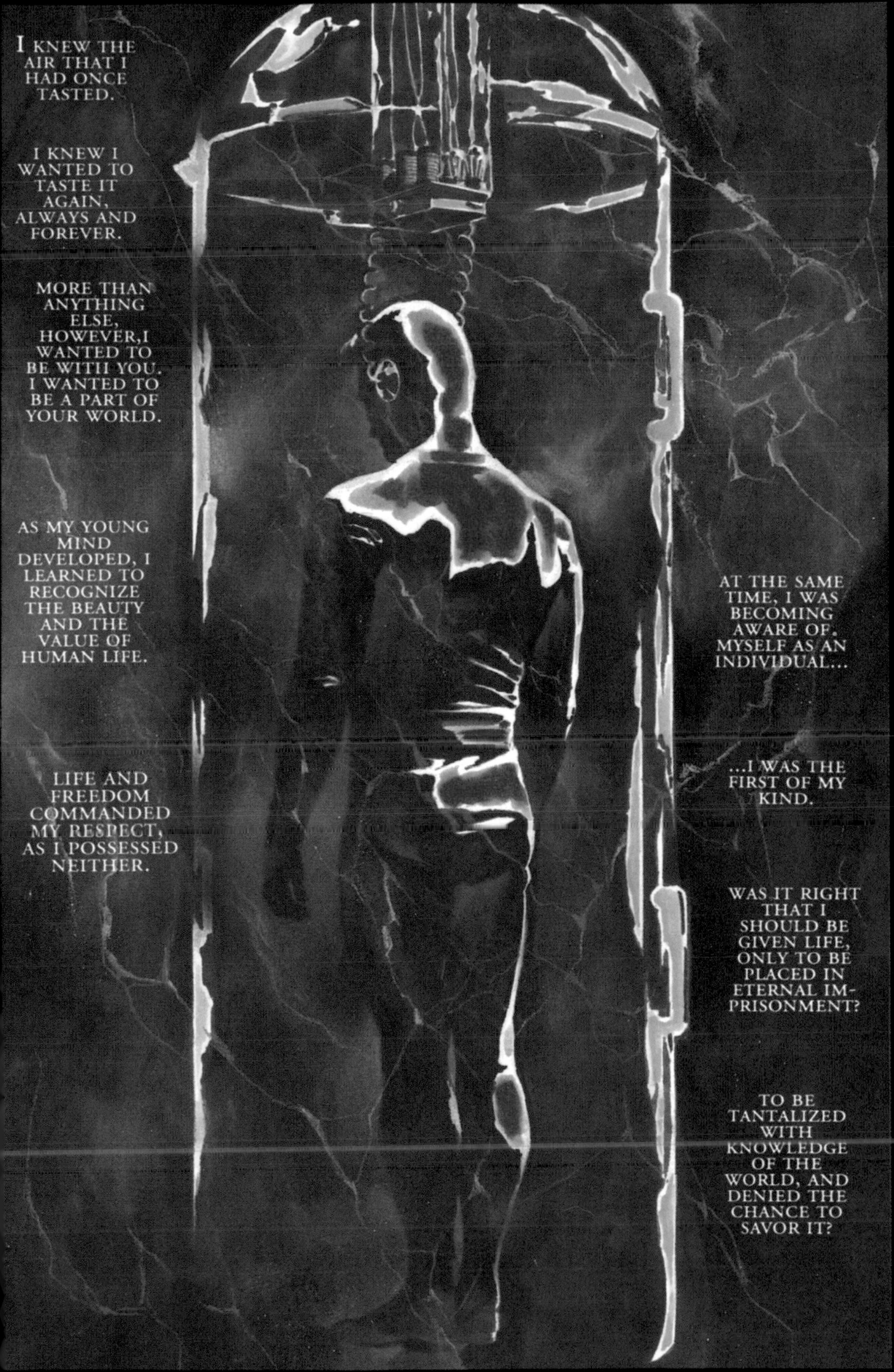

I KNEW THE AIR THAT I HAD ONCE TASTED.

I KNEW I WANTED TO TASTE IT AGAIN, ALWAYS AND FOREVER.

MORE THAN ANYTHING ELSE, HOWEVER, I WANTED TO BE WITH YOU. I WANTED TO BE A PART OF YOUR WORLD.

AS MY YOUNG MIND DEVELOPED, I LEARNED TO RECOGNIZE THE BEAUTY AND THE VALUE OF HUMAN LIFE.

LIFE AND FREEDOM COMMANDED MY RESPECT, AS I POSSESSED NEITHER.

AT THE SAME TIME, I WAS BECOMING AWARE OF MYSELF AS AN INDIVIDUAL...

...I WAS THE FIRST OF MY KIND.

WAS IT RIGHT THAT I SHOULD BE GIVEN LIFE, ONLY TO BE PLACED IN ETERNAL IMPRISONMENT?

TO BE TANTALIZED WITH KNOWLEDGE OF THE WORLD, AND DENIED THE CHANCE TO SAVOR IT?

SALVATION FINALLY CAME.

A TINY CRACK IN MY CONCRETE SURROUNDINGS BROUGHT IN THE SWEET AIR THAT I HAD CRAVED FOR SO LONG.

IN ONE ABRUPT MOMENT, A CATACLYSMIC BURST OF COLOR, LIGHT AND SOUND –

I WAS FREE.

AS AT THE MOMENT OF MY BIRTH.

I SCREAMED.

I WAS FINALLY FREE TO BREATHE AGAIN – TO FEEL THE RUSH OF HEAT ANIMATE MY FRAME.

MY FATHER TRIED TO CALL ME BACK...

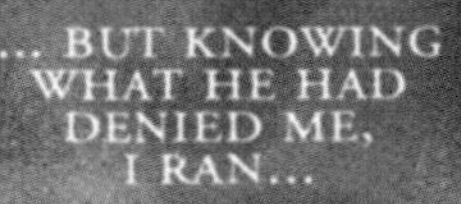

... BUT KNOWING WHAT HE HAD DENIED ME, I RAN...

...AFRAID OF BEING IMPRISONED AGAIN.

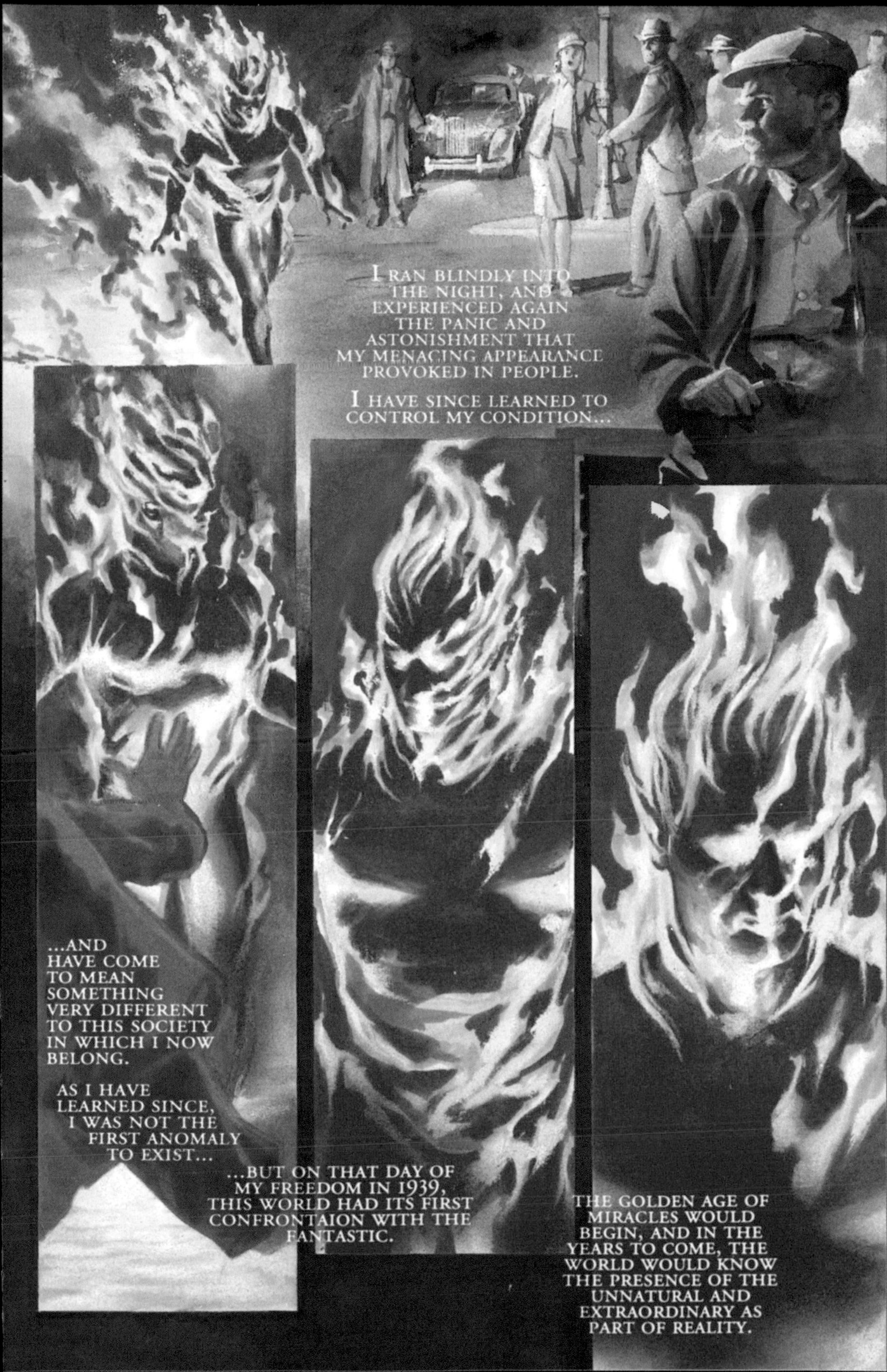

I RAN BLINDLY INTO THE NIGHT, AND EXPERIENCED AGAIN THE PANIC AND ASTONISHMENT THAT MY MENACING APPEARANCE PROVOKED IN PEOPLE.

I HAVE SINCE LEARNED TO CONTROL MY CONDITION...

...AND HAVE COME TO MEAN SOMETHING VERY DIFFERENT TO THIS SOCIETY IN WHICH I NOW BELONG.

AS I HAVE LEARNED SINCE, I WAS NOT THE FIRST ANOMALY TO EXIST...

...BUT ON THAT DAY OF MY FREEDOM IN 1939, THIS WORLD HAD ITS FIRST CONFRONTAION WITH THE FANTASTIC.

THE GOLDEN AGE OF MIRACLES WOULD BEGIN, AND IN THE YEARS TO COME, THE WORLD WOULD KNOW THE PRESENCE OF THE UNNATURAL AND EXTRAORDINARY AS PART OF REALITY.

MARVEL COMICS
ENTER: the X-MEN
UNTOLD TALES of
SPIDER-MAN
SPIDER-MAN
MAY'97 21
ONLY 99¢

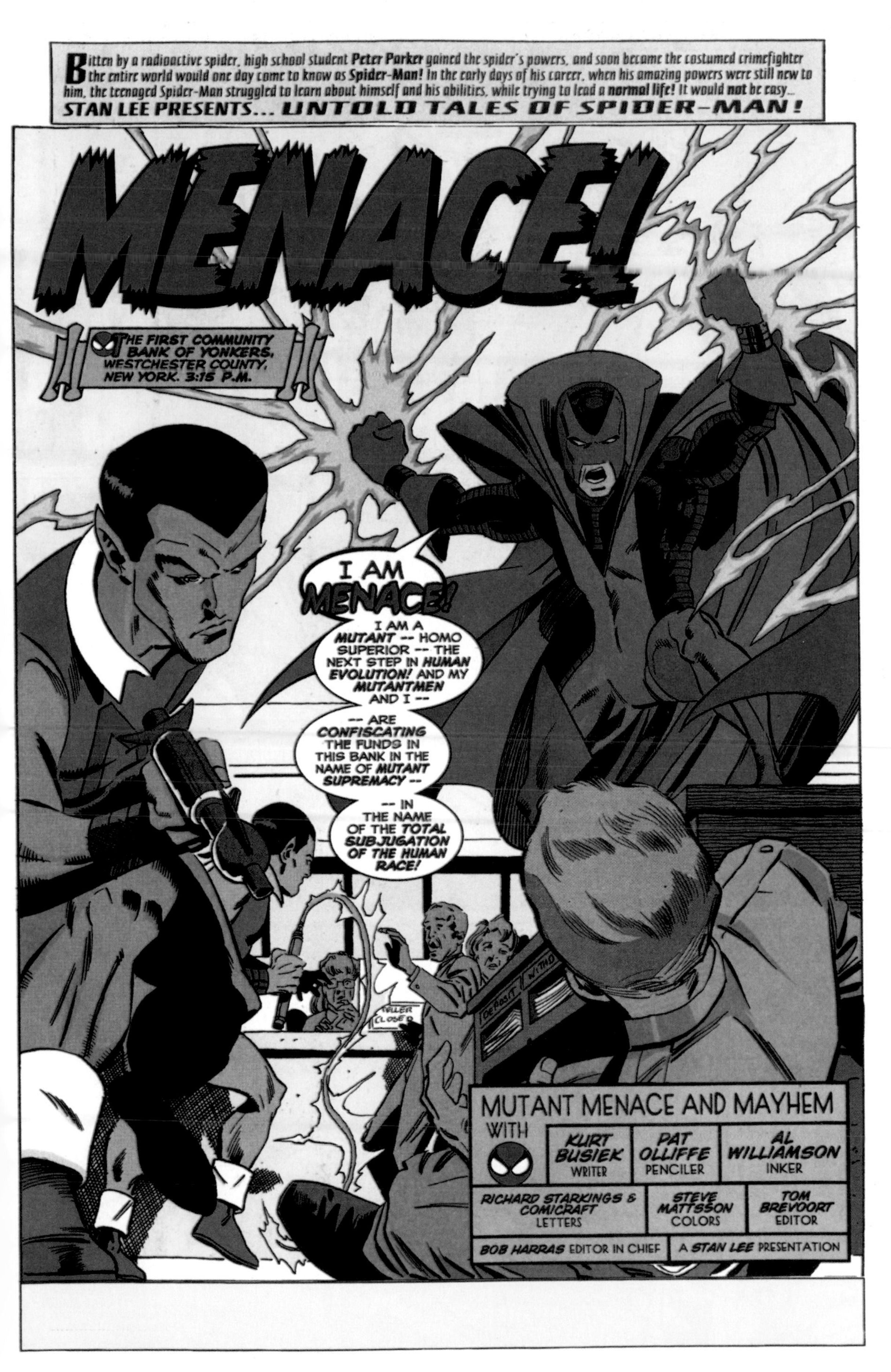

Bitten by a radioactive spider, high school student Peter Parker gained the spider's powers, and soon became the costumed crimefighter the entire world would one day come to know as Spider-Man! In the early days of his career, when his amazing powers were still new to him, the teenaged Spider-Man struggled to learn about himself and his abilities, while trying to lead a normal life! It would not be easy...
STAN LEE PRESENTS... UNTOLD TALES OF SPIDER-MAN!
MENACE!
THE FIRST COMMUNITY BANK OF YONKERS, WESTCHESTER COUNTY, NEW YORK. 3:15 P.M.
I AM MENACE!
I AM A MUTANT -- HOMO SUPERIOR -- THE NEXT STEP IN HUMAN EVOLUTION! AND MY MUTANTMEN AND I --
-- ARE CONFISCATING THE FUNDS IN THIS BANK IN THE NAME OF MUTANT SUPREMACY --
-- IN THE NAME OF THE TOTAL SUBJUGATION OF THE HUMAN RACE!
TELLER CLOSED
DEPOSIT
WITHD
MUTANT MENACE AND MAYHEM WITH
KURT BUSIEK WRITER
PAT OLLIFFE PENCILER
AL WILLIAMSON INKER
RICHARD STARKINGS & COMICRAFT LETTERS
STEVE MATTSSON COLORS
TOM BREVOORT EDITOR
BOB HARRAS EDITOR IN CHIEF
A STAN LEE PRESENTATION

THE CAMELOT TOWERS PENTHOUSE BALLROOM, PARK AVENUE, MANHATTAN. 3:27 P.M.
NO ONE IS SAFE! WE MUTANTS ARE EVERYWHERE -- AND ALL-POWERFUL!
SEE HOW EASILY I TELEPORT MYSELF AND MY MUTANTMEN FROM PLACE TO PLACE --
-- TO BLEED YOU INFERIOR HUMAN SWINE OF YOUR VALUABLES -- OF YOUR ILLUSION OF SECURITY --
-- AND IF YOU RESIST -- OF YOUR VERY LIVES!
THE GIDEON MUSEUM OF THE ARTS, FORT LEE, NEW JERSEY. 3:32 P.M.
YOUR TREASURES, YOUR JEWELRY -- ALL FORFEIT! FOR A NEW DAY IS DAWNING IN THIS WORLD --
-- A DAY WHEN MUTANTS SHALL TAKE THEIR RIGHTFUL PLACE AS RULERS OF THIS PLANET AND ALL UPON IT --
BODENSTEINER AVENUE, NASSAU COUNTY, LONG ISLAND. 3:39 P.M.
-- AND IT SHALL BE YOUR PRIVILEGE TO SERVE US -- AS NOTHING MORE THAN LOWLY SLAVES!
I AM MENACE, AND I GIVE YOU FAIR WARNING --
-- THAT YOUR TIME AS MASTERS OF THE EARTH IS OVER -- AND THE AGE OF THE MUTANT IS UPON YOU!
HA HA HA HA HA HA HA
THAT'S OUR PROLOGUE! NOW, ON TO OUR STORY, WHICH BEGINS A FEW EVENINGS LATER --

-- IN QUIET FOREST HILLS, HOME OF THE AMAZING SPIDER-MAN! BUT SPIDEY'S NOT WORRIED ABOUT SUPER-VILLAINS TONIGHT...
PETER... PETER...
I'M HERE, AUNT MAY. I'M HERE.
...NOT WHEN HIS AUNT MAY LIES AT DEATH'S DOOR, WEAKENED BY A MASSIVE HEART ATTACK...
GOT TO... GOT TO WATCH OVER HIM... PROMISED... RICHARD AND MARY... BUT... HE'S SO WITHDRAWN, SO FRAIL...
DON'T WORRY ABOUT ME, AUNT MAY. YOU JUST REST... REST AND RECOVER.
IF ONLY THERE WAS SOMETHING I COULD DO! BUT FOR ALL MY SPIDER-POWERS --I'M HELPLESS!
I OWE HER SO MUCH I CAN NEVER REPAY! AND NOW, SHE NEEDS ME --
-- AND I CAN'T EVEN GO OUT LOOKING FOR CRIME PHOTOS TO SELL TO THE BUGLE, IN ORDER TO PAY FOR HER MEDICINE. I JUST DON'T DARE LEAVE HER!
IT'S ALMOST FUNNY. THE WORLD THINKS SPIDEY'S A COWARD -- AFTER I RAN FROM A FIGHT WITH THE GREEN GOBLIN. IF THEY ONLY KNEW --!
PETER PARKER! YOU'LL MAKE YOURSELF ILL, SITTING AROUND AND FRETTING LIKE THIS! YOU'D BETTER LET ME WATCH MAY FOR A WHILE!
Mrs. WATSON! IT'S GOOD OF YOU TO OFFER, BUT YOU'VE DONE SO MUCH ALREADY -- TAKING CARE OF HER WHILE I'M IN SCHOOL --
Oh, PISH-TOSH! SHE'S MY FRIEND, IT'S NO BOTHER. AND YOU NEED TO GET OUT -- TO GET SOME AIR, TO SPEND SOME TIME WITH YOUR FRIENDS.
BUT Mrs. WATSON --
NOT ANOTHER WORD! NOW SCOOT!
AND SO, HEAVY-HEARTED, PETER PARKER WANDERS THROUGH THE GATHERING DUSK, HIS MIND BLANK, HIS FEET MOVING AUTOMATICALLY --
-- TAKING HIM, PERHAPS INEVITABLY, TO A SUBWAY ENTRANCE --

-- AND FROM THERE TO --
DAILY BUGLE
THE DAILY BUGLE. FIGURES I'D WIND UP HERE -- BUT I DON'T HAVE REASON TO GO IN. I'VE GOT NO PHOTOS TO SELL --
-- AND BETTY DOESN'T WANT TO SEE ME -- SHE'S MADE THAT PRETTY CLEAR. STILL, MAYBE IF I GO IN -- APOLOGIZE AGAIN --
PETER? PETER PARKER? OF ALL THE PEOPLE TO RUN INTO!
Huh? WHO --?
LIZ ALLAN! WHAT ARE YOU DOING IN MANHATTAN?
WELL, EITHER I'M CARRYING BOXES AND BAGS AROUND AS PART OF A NEW EXERCISE PROGRAM -- OR I'VE BEEN OUT SHOPPING!
IF YOU DON'T MIND MY SAYING SO, PETER -- YOU LOOK AWFUL!
YOU'VE GOT BAGS UNDER YOUR EYES, YOU'RE PALE -- YOU LOOK LIKE YOU HAVEN'T SLEPT IN DAYS!
IT'S NOT YOUR AUNT, IS IT? SHE'S -- SHE'S GOING TO BE OKAY, RIGHT?
WELL, THE DOCTORS SAY SHE'S GOT EVERY CHANCE -- AND THEY LET HER COME HOME, BUT...
Oh, PETER. IT MUST BE AWFUL. BUT STILL, YOU'VE GOT TO TAKE CARE OF YOURSELF, TOO. LET'S GO SOMEWHERE -- GET SOME FOOD INTO YOU...
WELL, I GUESS A GUY'S GOTTA EAT...
THAT'S THE SPIRIT, PAL. CAN'T HAVE THE SMARTEST BOY IN SCHOOL COLLAPSING FROM MALNUTRITION, CAN WE?
PETER FEELS HIS MOOD BEGINNING TO LIFT, AND EVEN SMILES, SLIGHTLY.
BUT HE MIGHT NOT FEEL QUITE THE SAME IF HE WERE TO LOOK BEHIND HIM AT THIS MOMENT...
I THOUGHT I SAW -- I DID! THERE'S PETER! AND HE'S WITH LIZ ALLAN AGAIN!
I TOLD MYSELF I WAS IMAGINING THINGS -- THAT I WAS OVERREACTING --

-- BUT I GUESS I WAS RIGHT THE FIRST TIME. FACE IT, BETTY BRANT -- YOU'VE LOST HIM!
BUT -- THAT'S WHAT YOU WANTED, ISN'T IT? OR... IS IT?
AND, UNAWARE OF THIS...
-- DON'T EVEN REMEMBER MY PARENTS. AUNT MAY AND UNCLE BEN -- THEY'VE BEEN THE ONLY FAMILY I'VE KNOWN.
AND SINCE UNCLE BEN DIED, AUNT MAY'S TAKEN SO MUCH ON HERSELF -- SCRIMPED AND SAVED, SACRIFICED --
YOU'RE LUCKY TO HAVE SOMEONE WHO CARES ABOUT YOU SO MUCH, PETER. FRANKLY, I'VE ALWAYS BEEN A LITTLE JEALOUS OF YOU FOR THAT...
REALLY? BUT YOUR DAD'S RICH -- HE'S GOT A HOTEL, A NIGHTCLUB --
YEAH, AND SINCE MY FOLKS SPLIT UP, I GET TO SEE HIM EVERY OTHER WEEKEND -- AND WHEN HE CAN SPARE THE TIME.
BUT HEY, LET'S NOT TALK ABOUT THIS. LET'S EAT.
THIS PLACE LOOKS GOOD.
WELL, IT'S NOT THE KIND OF PLACE I'D HAVE PICKED, BUT...
Oh, COME ON, PETER. WHAT COULD BE BETTER? IT'S A BEATNIK COFFEE-HOUSE -- WITH POETRY READINGS, YET!
IT'S A CHANGE OF PACE -- EXACTLY WHAT YOU NEED TO MAKE YOU FORGET YOUR TROUBLES FOR A LITTLE BIT!
THERE THEY WERE, A GENERATION... LOST, ALONE, OVERWHELMED...
IF YOU SAY SO, LIZ --
...THIRSTING FOR A WAKE-UP CALL, WITHOUT EVEN A TOOTHBRUSH...
-- BUT I HOPE THEY FLIP BURGERS BETTER THAN THAT GUY WRITES POETRY, OR THIS COULD BE AN EXCRUCIATING EXPERIENCE..!
SEE? NOW THERE'S THE PETER PARKER I REMEMBER...

BUT PETER AND LIZ AREN'T THE ONLY CUSTOMERS OF NOTE THIS EVENING...
SEE? DID I TELL YOU OR DID I TELL YOU? LOOK AT THIS PLACE! DRINK IN THE ATMOSPHERE! CHECK OUT THE CHICKS!
IF THIS ISN'T THE GREATEST LITTLE DIVE IN GREENWICH VILLAGE, I'M THE TOAD!
CAREFUL, ROBERT M'LAD! DON'T OVER-AGGRANDIZE THE ESTABLISHMENT -- OR IT'LL ASSUREDLY FALL SHORT OF OUR COMPATRIOTS' EXPECTATIONS!
HERE, JEAN -- LET ME HANG UP YOUR JACKET FOR YOU.
THANKS, WARREN...
WELL, BOBBY BOY? YOU ARE PAUSING LIKE A PROWLING PANTHER -- BUT THERE ARE PLENTY OF POTENTIAL PLACES TO PARK OUR POSTERIORS!
SORRY, HANK.
I JUST WANNA MAKE SURE WE SIT IN ZELDA'S SECTION.
I SWEAR, THAT LITTLE GAL MUST HAVE SUPER POWERS --
-- BECAUSE SHE MELTS MY FROSTY LITTLE HEART WITH NOTHING BUT A GLANCE!
SCOTT, YOU LOOK SO GRIM, SO SERIOUS! CAN'T YOU TAKE ONE NIGHT OFF, AND RELAX, WITH THE REST OF US?
SORRY, JEAN. WITH THE PROFESSOR AWAY, I'M A LITTLE DISTRACTED. PERHAPS I SHOULD HEAD BACK, LET THE REST OF YOU ENJOY YOURSELVES...
NONSENSE, SCOTT. NOW SIT DOWN -- THE WAITRESS IS HERE...
WHAT'LL IT BE, BIG SPENDER -- ONE CUP, FIVE WAYS?
NO WAY, ZEL -- MY PAL WARREN'S LUMPY WITH LOOT!
COFFEE ALL AROUND, A BASKET OF FRIES -- AND MENUS!
WHAT IS IT, HANK? WHAT HAVE YOU NOTICED?
PERHAPS NOTHING. IT'S THE HEADLINE ON YON FELLOW'S BROADSHEET...
MUTANTS, PFAH! THAT'S ALL YOU HEAR ABOUT THESE DAYS -- THE WAY THEY'RE ALL AROUND US, WAITING FOR THEIR CHANCE TO STRIKE!
DAILY BUGLE
MENACE STRIKES
MUTANT ROBBERIES INCREASE IN FREQUENCY!

THE GOVERNMENT OUGHT TO ROUND'EM ALL UP, AND SEND'EM ALL BACK TO, Uh...
WELL, THEY OUGHTTA DO SOMETHING ABOUT'EM!
BRR! MUTANTS -- JUST THE THOUGHT OF THEM MAKES MY SKIN CRAWL! WHY, THERE COULD BE MUTANTS HERE RIGHT NOW, AND WE WOULDN'T KNOW!
DON'T BE RIDICULOUS, LIZ. I EXPECT THERE ARE MUTANTS IN THE AREA, BUT THEY ARE NOT MONSTERS UNDER THE BED, OR AN EVIL CONSPIRACY--
-- THEY'RE JUST PEOPLE -- PEOPLE BORN WITH EXTRA POWERS OR ABILITIES, DUE TO GENETIC MUTATION. SOME OF 'EM'LL BE BAD APPLES, SURE --
-- BUT SOME'LL BE GOOD EGGS, TOO -- JUST LIKE PEOPLE EVERYWHERE!
LEND AN EAR, COMPEERS! THIS PERSPICACIOUS FELLOW'S TALKING SENSE -- UNLIKE MUCH OF THIS MUDDLED MODERN WORLD!
PEOPLE ARE SCARED OF MUTANTS BECAUSE THEY FEAR THE UNKNOWN -- BUT THERE'S REALLY NO REASON FOR IT!
WE DON'T FEAR ALL HUMANS BECAUSE SOME OF 'EM ARE CROOKS, DO WE?
AT THAT MOMENT, AT THE NEARBY OFFICES OF THE VAN LUNT TRADING COMPANY --
-- BUSINESS STILL BUSTLES, DESPITE THE HOUR --
-- BUT --
KRKAMM
COWER, HUMANS, FOR MENACE HAS ARRIVED --
-- THANKS TO THE DREAD POWER OF TELEPORTATION --
-- AND THE HOUR OF THE MUTANT IS UPON YOU!

SWIFTLY, THE MUTANTMEN ROUND UP THE COMPANY'S EMPLOYEES, AND SECURE THEM IN ONE AREA --
IN NOW!
W-WHAT DO YOU WANT!?!
SILENCE, HUMAN! YOU'LL GET YOUR TURN, IF I FAIL TO GET SATISFACTION FROM YOUR MANAGER, HERE!
AND NOW, PUNY WORM --
-- TASTE THE RIGHT THAT IS MY BIRTHRIGHT, THE POWER THAT MARKS ME FOREVER AS YOUR SUPERIOR!
YOU HOARD WEALTH HERE -- WEALTH IN THE FORM OF BEARER BONDS AND NEGOTIABLE SECURITIES!
KZAKK
UKHH!
THE MUTANT SUPREMACY REQUIRES THIS WEALTH -- TO FUND OUR HIDDEN LEGIONS, AND HASTEN THE END OF HUMANITY'S REIGN!
THUS, YOU HAVE A CHOICE TONIGHT: TURN OVER TO US WHAT WE SEEK, AND LIVE AS A SLAVE --
-- OR RESIST, AND DIE WHERE YOU GROVEL!
BUT NEARBY --
-- ONE EMPLOYEE, OVERLOOKED BY THE MUTANTMEN --
H-HID IN THE MEN'S-ROOM STALL -- ESCAPED THEIR NOTICE!
A-AND NOW -- I'M FREE!
GOT TO RUN -- GET TO A PHONE! CALL THE POLICE!
BUT FIRST --
-- GOT TO GET AWAY! OUT OF RANGE OF -- THEIR AWFUL POWERS!
MEANWHILE...
SO, PETER -- ARE YOU STILL SEEING THAT OLDER WOMAN? MISS BRANT?
BETTY? SHE'S NOT THAT MUCH OLDER THAN --

BUT BEFORE PETER CAN FINISH HIS SENTENCE --
QUICK! CALL THE POLICE! CALL THE ARMY!
MUTANTS -- AT VAN LUNT TRADING! THEY'VE TAKEN OVER -- THEY'RE KILLING THE EMPLOYEES! CALL THE AVENGERS -- CALL SOMEBODY!
HUH !?!
MOST OF THE COFFEE-HOUSE'S CUSTOMERS ARE STUNNED INTO IMMOBILITY BY THE STARTLING NEWS! BUT AT ONE PARTICULAR TABLE --
-- NO, NOT THIS ONE --
HEADS UP, HALCYON HEROES! IF THERE WAS EVER AN OCCURRENCE THAT MERITED OUR ATTENTION -- THIS IS SURELY IT!
YEAH, SO WE CAN SAVE THE LIVES OF SOME INGRATES WHO'D RATHER SEE US JAILED -- OR SHOT!
QUIET, BOTH OF YOU!
YOU KNEW THE SITUATION WHEN YOU JOINED THE TEAM! NOW, MOVE -- WE'LL CHANGE INTO OUR COSTUMES IN THE ALLEY!
AND EVEN AS THE FIVE MYSTERIOUS TEENAGERS BOLT FOR THE DOOR --
-- ANOTHER ISN'T FAR BEHIND!
SOUNDS LIKE SPIDEY MIGHT BE NEEDED! BESIDES --
-- I CAN'T PASS UP THE CHANCE TO GET SOME NEWS PIX --
TO MAKE THE MONEY TO PAY FOR AUNT'S MAY MEDICINE!
SORRY, LIZ -- I'VE GOT TO GO!
GOT TO RUSTLE UP A CAMERA, AND GET OVER THERE -- THE BUGLE'LL NEED PHOTOGRAPHS!
B-BUT, PETER --
I'LL SEE YOU LATER!
BUT --
HMF!
FLASH THOMPSON NEVER RUNS OFF IN THE MIDDLE OF A DATE...!

AND SHORTLY, AT VAN LUNT TRADING --
P-PLEASE -- LET US --
SILENCE!
-- THE FIVE TEENAGERS FROM THE COFFEEHOUSE REAPPEAR, BUT IN A VERY DIFFERENT GUISE --
-- THAT OF THE STRANGEST HEROES OF ALL -- THE UNCANNY
X-MEN
INTRUDERS! X-MEN!
STOP THEM!
GOT THAT BACKWARDS, FELLA -- WE'RE HERE TO STOP YOU!
AND JUST BECAUSE I'M FIRING MY OPTIC BLAST AT LOW INTENSITY, SO AS TO PUT YOU DOWN WITHOUT INJURING YOU --
ZAKT
-- DON'T THINK WE'RE GOING TO TAKE IT EASY ON YOU! HIT 'EM, X-MEN -- HARD AND FAST!
NICE, MARVEL GIRL! YOUR TELEKINESIS SET HIM UP FOR ME PERFECTLY -- WE MAKE A GOOD TEAM!
WRAK
THANKS, ANGEL! BUT WE'RE ALL A TEAM -- FOLLOWING CYCLOPS'S LEAD!
HEY, BEAST -- CHECK IT OUT! INSTANT CROOKSICLES -- EACH IN THEIR OWN SNOW-COCOONS!!
EXEMPLARY, MY DEAR ICEMAN! AS FOR ME, MY PRODIGIOUS PEDAL EXTREMITIES HAVE THINGS WELL IN HAND -- OR FOOT, TO BE MORE ACCURATE!
BUT EVEN AS THE X-MEN ENGAGE THEIR FOES --
RUN! RUN! IT'S MORE OF THEM!
IT FIGURES! THEY'RE AS SCARED OF US AS THEY WERE OF THEIR CAPTORS!
CAN'T ANYONE EVER BE GLAD TO SEE US..?

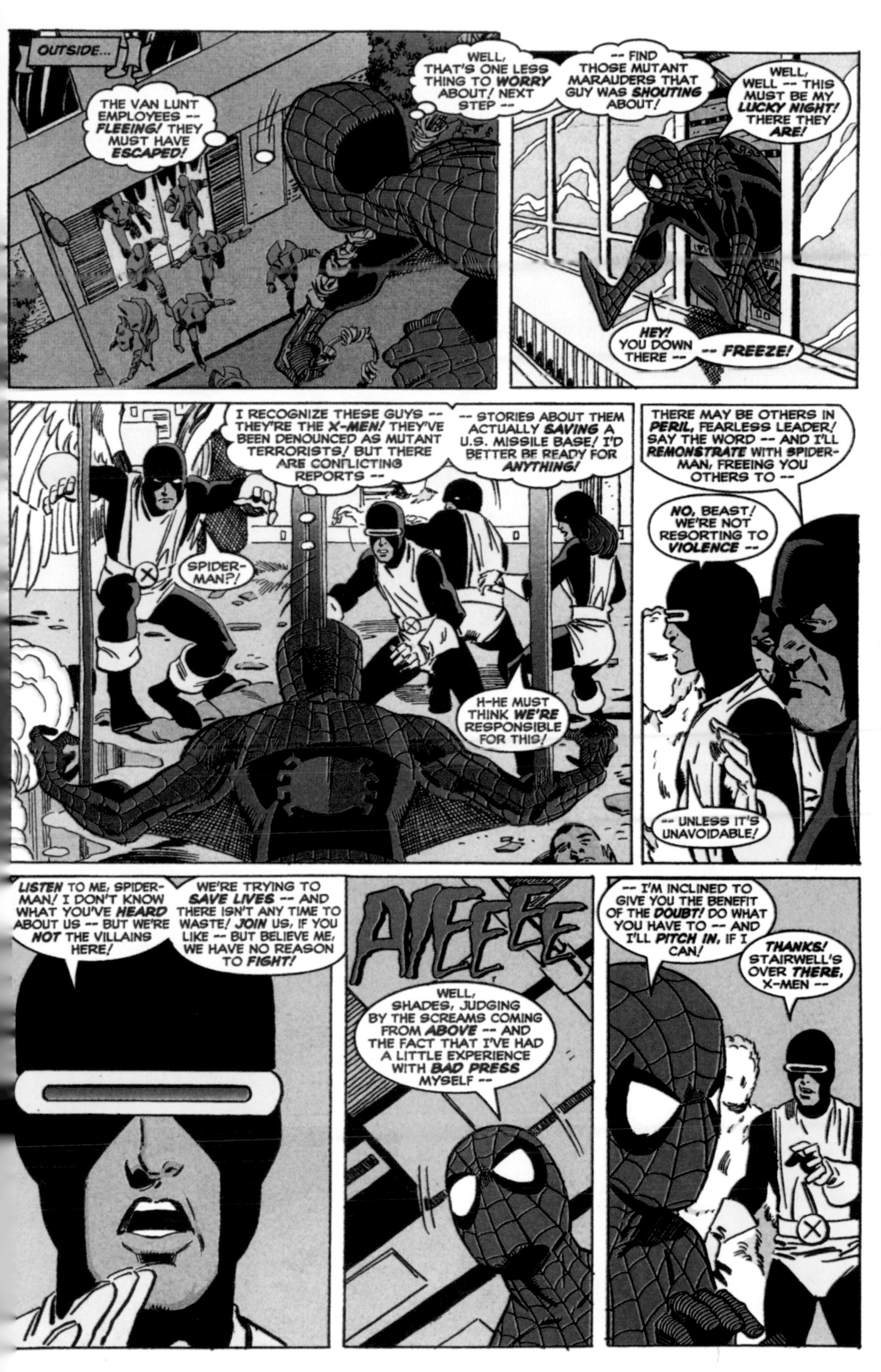

OUTSIDE...
THE VAN LUNT EMPLOYEES -- FLEEING! THEY MUST HAVE ESCAPED!
WELL, THAT'S ONE LESS THING TO WORRY ABOUT! NEXT STEP --
-- FIND THOSE MUTANT MARAUDERS THAT GUY WAS SHOUTING ABOUT!
WELL, WELL -- THIS MUST BE MY LUCKY NIGHT! THERE THEY ARE!
HEY! YOU DOWN THERE --
-- FREEZE!
I RECOGNIZE THESE GUYS -- THEY'RE THE X-MEN! THEY'VE BEEN DENOUNCED AS MUTANT TERRORISTS! BUT THERE ARE CONFLICTING REPORTS --
-- STORIES ABOUT THEM ACTUALLY SAVING A U.S. MISSILE BASE! I'D BETTER BE READY FOR ANYTHING!
SPIDER-MAN?!
H-HE MUST THINK WE'RE RESPONSIBLE FOR THIS!
THERE MAY BE OTHERS IN PERIL, FEARLESS LEADER! SAY THE WORD -- AND I'LL REMONSTRATE WITH SPIDER-MAN, FREEING YOU OTHERS TO --
NO, BEAST! WE'RE NOT RESORTING TO VIOLENCE --
-- UNLESS IT'S UNAVOIDABLE!
LISTEN TO ME, SPIDER-MAN! I DON'T KNOW WHAT YOU'VE HEARD ABOUT US -- BUT WE'RE NOT THE VILLAINS HERE!
WE'RE TRYING TO SAVE LIVES -- AND THERE ISN'T ANY TIME TO WASTE! JOIN US, IF YOU LIKE -- WE HAVE NO REASON TO FIGHT!
AIEEEE
WELL, SHADES, JUDGING BY THE SCREAMS COMING FROM ABOVE -- AND THE FACT THAT I'VE HAD A LITTLE EXPERIENCE WITH BAD PRESS MYSELF --
-- I'M INCLINED TO GIVE YOU THE BENEFIT OF THE DOUBT! DO WHAT YOU HAVE TO -- AND I'LL PITCH IN, IF I CAN!
THANKS! STAIRWELL'S OVER THERE, X-MEN --

"-- LET'S GO!"
YOU'VE ONLY FELT A FRACTION OF MY POWER SO FAR, HUMAN! NOW SPEAK -- OR I REDUCE YOUR HEAD TO A CINDER!
P-PLEASE --! I'VE GOT A WIFE -- KIDS! THE BONDS ARE IN A SAFE -- I-IN Mr. WILKIN'S OFFICE! B-BUT I D-DON'T KNOW THE COMBINATION --!
NO MATTER! THE SAFE HAS NOT BEEN BUILT THAT CAN WITHSTAND MY MUTANT POWER! LEAD ME TO IT -- AND YOUR LIFE IS SPARED!
BUT AT THAT MOMENT...
HEY -- IT'S THAT MENACE CHARACTER! I'VE BEEN ITCHING FOR A CHANCE AT HIM, THE WAY HE'S BEEN MAKING MUTANTS LOOK BAD!
WATCH OUT, KIDS -- THE ARTICLES SAID HE'S A TELEPORTER, LIKE THE VANISHER!
THE X-MEN?!
WH KAM
AND SPIDER-MAN -- DON'T FORGET ABOUT ME!
YOU CAN TELL I'M A RINGER -- 'CAUSE I'M NOT WEARING THE SCHOOL COLORS!
Bah! I HAVE NO TIME FOR THIS! DEAL WITH THEM, MY MUTANTMEN --
-- WHILE I ATTEND TO OUR PRIMARY OBJECTIVE!
SURRENDER, X-MEN!
SURRENDER, OR DIE!
WHOA! I KNOW HOW THIS SCENE PLAYS OUT, FELLAS 'N'GALS! I'VE PLAYED IT OFTEN ENOUGH MYSELF!
WHY DON'T YOU WALTZ AROUND WITH THESE CHEERFUL CHARLIES, X-FOLKS --
-- WHILE I MAKE TRACKS AFTER THE HEAD CHEESE!

A HEAD-ON ASSAULT AGAINST A GUY WHO CAN TELEPORT ISN'T THE SMARTEST OF IDEAS -- SO MAYBE I'D BETTER TRY A LESS DIRECT ROUTE!
AND THIS VENTILATION GRID LOOKS LIKE JUST THE TICKET!
RRAKK
LOOKS PRETTY SIMPLE -- THE VENTILATION SYSTEM RUNS IN A LINE PAST ALL THE BACK OFFICES!
THEY SHOULD ALL BE DESERTED AT THIS HOUR -- SO ALL I HAVE TO DO IS FOLLOW THE SLIGHTEST SOUND...!
AND, SURE ENOUGH --
WHERE ARE YOU, LITTLE OFFICE SAFE? STUFFED WITH SECURITIES -- BULGING WITH BONDS!
COME TO PAPA...
SHKK
Ah!
TEAM ALPHA TO TEAM BETA! HOLD OFF -- REPEAT, HOLD OFF UNTIL YOU GET THE CLEAR-SIGNAL FROM ME!
WE HAVE REACHED THE OBJECTIVE -- AND THINGS ARE UNDER CONTROL -- BUT THERE'S BEEN A DELAY!
HOLD YOUR POSITION AND WAIT 'TIL YOU HEAR FROM ME. TEAM ALPHA OUT!
"TEAM ALPHA"?
"COME TO PAPA"? WHAT'S HE UP TO -- AND WHY DOES HE SUDDENLY SOUND COMPLETELY DIFFERENT?
OKAY, LITTLE SAFE -- LET'S SEE JUST HOW TOUGH YOU ARE...
I REALLY SHOULD HANG BACK -- TAKE SOME PHOTOS! BUT I'VE GOT TO ADMIT --

-- I'M JUST TOO DARN CURIOUS!
BRANGG
HEY! DENNIS! SORRY TO INTERRUPT AND ALL --
Huh?
I-I MEAN -- EhP!
-- BUT THE COPS WOULD LIKE A WORD WITH YOU! YOU CAN SPARE A LITTLE TIME, CAN'T YOU -- SAY, FIVE TO FIFTEEN?!
BAH! YOU ARE NOTHING MORE THAN A MINOR NUISANCE, SPIDER-MAN! FOR I AM MENACE --
-- AND MY MUTANT POWERS GIVE ME THE TOUCH OF DEATH!
AND NOW WE'RE BACK TO SUPER-VILLAIN SPEECH PATTERN #1! JUST WHAT GOES ON HERE ANYWAY?!
HEY, NOW, FELLA -- IS THAT NICE? IS THAT POLITE?
IS THAT HOW YOUR MOTHER BROUGHT YOU UP -- TO GET GRABBY WITH TOTAL STRANGERS ON A FIRST DATE?
ME, I'D NEVER DO A THING LIKE THAT --
-- NOT WHEN I CAN ZAP YOU IN THE FACE WITH A DOUBLE HANDFUL OF WEBBING, ANYWAY!
THWIPP THWIPP
Uhh! MY FACE!
YOUR EFFORTS ARE DOOMED TO FAILURE, SPIDER-MAN -- FOR I AM YOUR SUPERIOR IN EVERY WAY!
MY HELMET PROTECTS ME FROM YOUR CRAVEN ATTACK -- AND MY POWER CAN SEAR YOUR WEBBING AWAY LIKE IT NEVER EXISTED! BUT I ASK YOU --
-- WHAT WILL SAVE YOU FROM ME?!

AND AS SPIDER-MAN DODGES FRANTICALLY -- BACK AT THE COFFEEHOUSE...
HI, FLASH!
THANKS FOR COMING TO GET ME -- I REALLY DIDN'T LIKE THE IDEA OF RIDING THE SUBWAY BACK OUT TO QUEENS AT THIS HOUR!
DE NADA, LIZ. WHAT ARE FRIENDS FOR?
HOP OVER INTO THE BACK, JASON -- YOU KNOW THOMPSON'S RULE!
YEAH, YEAH -- BLONDES GET THE FRONT SEAT, I KNOW!
WHOOPS! SORRY 'BOUT THAT, FLASH --
-- BUT I SEEM TO HAVE KNOCKED OVER YOUR LAUNDRY!
HUH? FLASH THOMPSON -- WHAT ARE YOU DOING WITH A SPIDER-MAN COSTUME?! YOU'RE NOT GOING TO DO ANYTHING CRAZY, ARE YOU?
CRAZY? OUR PAL FLASH? NO WAY, LIZ! UNLESS, OF COURSE, IT'S CRAZY TO DRESS UP AS SPIDER-MAN, TO MAKE FOLKS THINK HE'S STILL AROUND --
-- EVEN THOUGH THAT YELLOW-BELLIED WEB-SLINGER HASN'T DARED TO SHOW HIMSELF IN A WEEK!
ENOUGH, JASON!
NOBODY SLAMS SPIDEY -- NOT IN MY CAR! HE MUST'VE HAD A REASON FOR DISAPPEARING -- MAYBE HE'S ON A SECRET MISSION OR SOMETHING!
BUT HE'S NOT A COWARD -- YOU'LL SEE!
WELL, WHETHER HE IS OR ISN'T A COWARD, FLASH -- DON'T EVEN THINK ABOUT GOING OUT DRESSED LIKE THAT!
IT'S DANGEROUS! YOU COULD GET SERIOUSLY HURT -- OR WORSE!
AW, YOU SOUND LIKE MY GRANDMA, LIZ! BUT DON'T WORRY, I WAS ONLY THINKIN' ABOUT IT. OL' SPIDEY DOESN'T NEED MY HELP, ANYWAY --

"HE CAN TAKE CARE OF HIMSELF!"
I SHOULDN'T HAVE CHALLENGED HIM IN SUCH AN ENCLOSED SPACE!
HE CAN BLAST EVERY WHICH WAY, TRYING TO CUT ME DOWN, AND I --
--I DON'T HAVE THAT MUCH ROOM TO DODGE!
FALL, SPIDER-MAN, FALL!
FOR ALL THAT MY SPIDER-SENSE HELPS KEEP ME AHEAD OF HIM, SOONER OR LATER HE'S GOING TO --
AIIKKH!
Uhhh! SEARING PAIN -- LIKE AN ELECTRICAL BLAST, BUT --
DO YOU FEEL IT, SPIDER-MAN? THE POISON OF MY MUTANT POWER -- ENTERING YOUR BLOOD-STREAM -- SETTING YOUR NERVES AFIRE!
YOU'RE SUCCUMBING --
AND SOON, YOU WON'T BE ABLE TO MOVE AT ALL!
ARMS -- LIKE LEAD! HE'S GOT ME AT HIS MERCY -- HE'S GOING TO KILL ME --
-- AND AUNT MAY --
-- I'M SORRY, AUNT MAY -- I SHOULDN'T HAVE BEEN SO FOOLISH -- SHOULDN'T HAVE RISKED MY LIFE, WHEN YOU'RE SO --
BUT YOU'LL NEVER FEEL THE FULL PARALYSIS, WALL-CRAWLER! BECAUSE WITH MY NEXT TOUCH, YOU'LL BE -- Eh?!
TEAM ALPHA -- THIS IS TEAM GAMMA! WHAT'S THE HOLD-UP?
YOU KNOW, MENACE, SOMETHING'S NOT KOSHER HERE AND I THINK I'VE GOT AN IDEA WHAT IT IS!

BUT I'VE GOT TO THANK YOUR BUDDY ON THE OTHER END OF THAT RADIO-LINK, FOR GIVING ME A CHANCE TO CATCH MY BREATH --
-- AND TO REALIZE THAT THAT JOLT YOU HIT ME WITH WASN'T ANYWHERE NEAR AS BAD AS YOU WERE MAKING IT OUT TO BE!
WRAKK
UHH!
AND NOW --
-- LET'S TAKE A LOOK AT THAT ARMOR OF YOURS!
SHREDD
I KNEW IT! YOU ARE NOT A MUTANT AT ALL! YOU'RE JUST A FRAUD IN AN ELECTRICAL HARNESS, PLAYING ON PEOPLE'S FEAR TO ROB THEM --
-- TO INTIMIDATE THEM WITH TALK OF CONSPIRACIES AND SPOOKY POWERS! YOU MISERABLE SLIME --!
SLIME!? I'M DOING MANKIND A SERVICE, JERK -- AWAKENING THEM TO THE THREAT OF MUTANTS IN THEIR MIDST!
OH, AND ISN'T THAT ADMIRABLE! YOU KNOW, MENACE...
...GIVEN A CHOICE BETWEEN BEING A HUMAN LIKE YOU, AND A MUTANT LIKE THOSE X-MEN OUT THERE --
"-- I'D PICK A 'MUTANT', EVERY TIME!"
X-MEN! CALL ME OVERANALYTICAL, IF YOU WILL, BUT THE MANNER IN WHICH THESE ERSATZ STORM-TROOPERS MOVE --
-- THE WAY THEY FIGHT, THE WAY THEY SPEAK, ON THOSE RARE OCCASIONS THAT THEY DO LET FLY WITH VERBIAGE --
-- DOES IT STRIKE ANYONE BUT MY EVER-REBOUNDING SELF AS A TRIFLE... IDENTICAL?
WKAMM

I'D BEEN NOTICING THAT MYSELF, BEAST! THEY DON'T ACT LIKE INDIVIDUALS -- BUT LIKE MULTIPLE COPIES OF THE SAME BEING! LIKE CLONES, OR --
KRAM
HOLY HANNAH!
PAY NO ATTENTION TO THE MAN BEHIND THE CURTAIN, X-MEN -- IT SEEMS THE GREAT AND POWERFUL OZ IS NOTHING BUT A HUMBUG!
THAT MACHINERY --!
THIS CASTS AN ENTIRELY NEW COMPLEXION ON THE MATTER BEFORE US, DOESN'T IT? IF MENACE ISN'T A MUTANT AFTER ALL --
-- THEN PERHAPS HIS MALEVOLENT MINIONS ARE LESS THAN THEY APPEAR, AS WELL! AND IF I SURMISE CORRECTLY, BASED ON HIS POWER-CIRCUITRY --
-- SPIDER-MAN! HIS WRIST-CONTROLS -- DISCOMBOBULATE THEM!
YOU GOT IT, BEAST! ANYONE WHO USES AS MANY BIG WORDS AS YOU -- I'VE GOT TO FIGURE HE KNOWS SOMETHING!
KRNCH
KRNCH
AND NO SOONER HAS SPIDER-MAN CRUSHED MENACE'S GAUNTLETS, THEN --
THE MUTANTMEN!
THEY -- THEY WERE --
-- ROBOTS!
KZAK
KZAK
KZAK
KZAK

OKAY, I'M THE KID HERE, I DON'T MIND LOOKING DUMB --
-- WHAT TIPPED YOU OFF, SPIDER-MAN? HOW'D YOU FIGURE OUT HE WASN'T A MUTANT?
HE PUSHED IT TOO HARD, MOSTLY --
-- KEPT ON TALKING ABOUT WHAT A MENACING, DANGEROUS MUTANT HE WAS, AS IF HE WAS TRYING TO CONVINCE ME.
PLUS, HE TRIED TO MAKE IT LOOK LIKE HE COULD TELEPORT, BUT HE NEVER ACTUALLY DID. SO WHEN I HEARD HIS RADIO GO OFF --
-- I FIGURED HE WASN'T WHO HE SAID HE WAS.
MY GUESS IS, THERE ARE FOUR OR FIVE "MENACES," AND THEY TIME THEIR STRIKES TO MAKE IT LOOK LIKE THEY'RE ONE GUY, TELEPORTING --
-- IT BOOSTS PEOPLE'S FEAR AND MAKES IT EASIER TO GET AWAY, IF THE COPS ARE LOOKING FOR YOU IN ANOTHER BOROUGH.
NOT BAD, SMART GUY -- THE ONLY BIT YOU MISSED WAS OUR LUCKIN' INTO THOSE ROBOTS, WITH THE LOOT FROM OUR FIRST FEW JOBS --
-- AND HAVING 'EM CUSTOMIZED UP TO LOOK LIKE MUTANT FREAKS! BUT IT WON'T HELP YOU -- NONE OF IT!
ONCE THIS GETS TO COURT, I'M STILL HUMAN -- AND YOU X-CREEPS ARE MUTANTS! I WON'T EVEN ADMIT SPIDER-MAN WAS INVOLVED --
-- IT'LL JUST BE A CASE OF AN INNOCENT HUMAN, FRAMED BY SLIMY MUTIES!
TELL ME -- HAVE YOU EVER MET J. JONAH JAMESON?
HAH! BLOW IT OUT YOUR EAR -- THE BUNCH OF YOU! YOU CAN'T TOUCH ME!
MAYBE WE CAN. WE'VE GOT YOUR EQUIPMENT -- AND THE BURNT-OUT ROBOTS, OF COURSE. AND IF WE MOVE FAST --
-- MAYBE WE CAN TRACK DOWN YOUR PARTNERS BEFORE THEY REALIZE THEIR COVER'S BLOWN.
IF THEY'RE ANYWHERE NEAR AS SMART AS YOU, THAT SHOULDN'T BE HARD.

WHAT DO YOU SAY, SPIDER-MAN? LIKE TO COME ALONG AND LEND A HAND? SEE THINGS THROUGH TO THE END?
Huh?
I, Uh -- I CAN'T! SORRY, BUT YOU'LL HAVE TO HANDLE IT YOURSELVES!
WH --?
BUT GOOD LUCK, THOUGH -- I'M SURE YOU DON'T NEED ME ALONG, ANYWAY!
HMP. CAST TOGETHER WITH MUTANTS BY MISCHANCE, HE MAKES THE BEST OF IT, BUT ALLOW HIM A MOMENT TO COGITATE -- AND HE BOLTS.
NOT THE WORST TREATMENT WE'VE EVER ENCOUNTERED, BUT DISAPPOINTING NONETHELESS.
SIGH IF ONLY SPIDER-MAN WERE MORE LIKE THAT YOUNG FELLOW AT THE DINING ESTABLISHMENT.
IF ONLY THE WORLD WAS...
AND, OUTSIDE...
I HATED TO DO THAT -- AND I KNOW WHAT THEY MUST THINK OF ME. BUT I COULDN'T GO WITH THEM -- I JUST COULDN'T!
I CAN'T GO INTO BATTLE -- RISK MY LIFE, AND MAYBE LOSE IT -- WITH AUNT MAY AS SICK AS SHE IS!
I'M ALL SHE'S GOT! IF I WERE TO GET HURT, OR KILLED -- SHE'D BE ALONE! AND WHATEVER MY RESPONSIBILITIES TO THE WORLD --
-- MY RESPONSIBILITY TO HER HAS TO COME FIRST! I FAILED UNCLE BEN -- I CAN'T FAIL HER! NOT EVEN IF IT SHOULD MEAN --
-- THAT I CAN NEVER BECOME SPIDER-MAN AGAIN!
NEXT:
THE WORLD THINKS SPIDER-MAN'S A COWARD!
HAS IT FINALLY COME TRUE? YOU'LL HAVE TO ASK..
BOO!
THE SCARECROW!

CHEN
Cannon
LIQUID!

GOOD AFTER-NOON.
THIS IS CHESS ROBERTS, CBNC -- AND ONCE AGAIN, BUZZ IN THE BUSINESS WORLD CENTERS ON ONE MAN --
-- BILLIONAIRE BUSINESSMAN AND INVENTOR ANTHONY STARK.
CBNC
ONLY DAYS AGO, THE CALIFORNIA STATE PROBATE COURT DECLARED THAT STARK, THOUGHT DEAD FOR MONTHS, WAS IN FACT ALIVE --
-- AND ENTITLED TO RETAKE THE REINS OF HIS ESTATE, INCLUDING HIS PERSONAL FORTUNE AND HIS EXTENSIVE INVESTMENT PORTFOLIO.
TODAY, THE OFTEN-CONTROVERSIAL GENIUS ANNOUNCED HE'S CLOSED A DEAL TO PURCHASE A SKYSCRAPER IN MANHATTAN'S FLATIRON DISTRICT --
-- AND WOULD MAKE IT HIS NEW YORK HEAD-QUARTERS.
RENOVATIONS TO THE BUILDING WERE MADE DURING NEGOTIATIONS --
-- AND THE HOT TICKET IN NEW YORK TONIGHT IS AN INVITATION TO THE COMBINED RECHRISTENING-RESURRECTION PARTY STARK IS THROWING.
BUT TO MOST NEW YORKERS, STARK'S LEGAL AND FINANCIAL DEVELOPMENTS TAKE A BACK SEAT TO THE NEWS --
LOOK! COMING OUT OF THE SUN!
IS THAT -- IS THAT --
YES!
IT'S -- IT'S HIM!

-- THAT IRON MAN, STARK'S INTERNATIONALLY-CELEBRATED ARMORED BODYGUARD, WOULD SOON BE BACK IN ACTION AS WELL.
ACCORDING TO STARK, HIS DEATH WAS FAKED BY TERRORISTS WHO'D KIDNAPPED HIM IN ORDER TO FORCE HIM TO DESIGN WEAPONS FOR THEM --
-- BUT HE WAS RESCUED -- AND THE TERRORISTS ROUTED -- AFTER IRON MAN RETURNED FROM SEEMING DEATH HIMSELF, ALONG WITH MANY OF THE WORLD'S OTHER HEROES.
IRON MAN'S ARMOR WAS BADLY DAMAGED, HOWEVER -- AND HE WAS SIDELINED UNTIL STARK COULD BUILD A NEW AND IMPROVED MODEL.
IRON MAN, WHO WAS A FOUNDING MEMBER OF THE MIGHTY AVENGERS, HAS FOR YEARS FOUGHT TO PROTECT THE WORLD FROM --
I MENTALLY TUNE OUT THE CBNC AUDIO FEED FOR A MINUTE OR TWO -- IT'S NOT LIKE I NEED TO HEAR IRON MAN'S RESUMÉ.
IT'D BE EASIER IF THE WORLD KNEW THAT UNDER THIS MASK, I AM TONY STARK --
-- THAT I WAS TRAPPED, ALONG WITH THE OTHERS, ON ANOTHER WORLD. A WORLD WE ALL ESCAPED-- EXCEPT FOR DOCTOR DOOM AND THOR.
CAMER
VIDEO

BUT THAT'S NOT A SECRET I'M WILLING TO SHARE. SO I GIVE THEM A COVER STORY, HIDE BEHIND MY NEWLY-REFURBISHED MASK --
-- AND I LISTEN TO THE WORLD TALK ABOUT ME.
-- QUESTION ON THE LIPS OF EVERYONE IN THE FINANCIAL COMMUNITY -- WILL STARK SEEK TO OVERTURN THE SALE OF STARK ENTERPRISES TO FUJIKAWA, INC. --
-- AND TAKE BACK CONTROL OF THE MULTI-NATIONAL CORPORATION HE BUILT FROM THE GROUND UP?
LOOKING FORWARD
KURT BUSIEK & SEAN CHEN
Special Thanks to Alex Ross & Allen Bujak, For Their Armor Design Contributions
Stan Lee presents
THE ARMORED AVENGER
ERIC CANNON Inks LIQUID! Colors
RS/COMICRAFT/DL Letters
BOBBIE CHASE Editor
BOB HARRAS Chief

SINCE THE SALE OCCURRED WHILE STARK WAS THOUGHT DEAD, ITS LEGALITY COULD BE CHALLENGED --
-- AND INDUSTRY ANALYSTS FEEL STARK COULD OVERTURN --
I SHUT IT OFF FOR GOOD THIS TIME. I DON'T WANT TO THINK ABOUT IT.
I'D RATHER JUST LUXURIATE IN THE FEELING OF FLIGHT -- IN THE THRUST OF MY BOOT-TURBINES, THE WIND WHISTLING BY --
-- MY INTERNAL SERVOS HUMMING SMOOTHLY AS MY ARMOR RESPONDS TO MY MENTAL COMMANDS.
EMBASSY 1
ALIVE
TARGET
THE REST CAN WAIT. I'M BACK. I'M ALIVE. I FEEL GOOD --
-- AND THE SIGHT I SEE AS I BANK WEST MAKES ME FEEL EVEN BETTER.
IT'LL BE A COMMUNITY CENTER WHEN IT'S FINISHED, TO SERVE SOME OF THE PEOPLE WHO HAD THEIR HOMES DESTROYED IN THE ONSLAUGHT MESS.
THE MARIA STARK FOUNDATION IS BUILDING IT. NICE TO KNOW THEY KEPT ROLLING WHILE I--
BRRT BRRT BRRT
MY PRIORITY ALARM.
IT'S A POLICE BAND REPORT, PIPED TO ME BY MY SCANNERS BECAUSE OF THE LEVEL OF THE THREAT. AND I RECOGNIZE THE ADDRESS.

THE AVALON TRADING COMPANY.
NOW, ACCORDING TO THE POLICE SQUEAL, GEORGIE AND HIS EMPLOYEES ARE UNDER SIEGE -- AND SHOTS HAVE BEEN FIRED.
THE POLIZEI -- THEY WILL JUST NOW BE DISCOVERING THAT THE ELEVATORS ARE OUT OF ORDER, AND WILL BE CALLING FOR HELICOPTERS.
BUT THANKS TO THE DEAD GENTLEMAN HERE, WHO GAVE UP THE COMBINATIONS AND PASSCODES WE NEED --
I WENT TO PREP SCHOOL WITH GEORGIE AVALON -- AND OUR FATHERS PLAYED GOLF TOGETHER WHENEVER THEY HAD THE CHANCE.
-- MY MEN AND I -- AND A FORTUNE IN NEGOTIABLE BONDS -- WILL BE AIRLIFTED AWAY AND OUT OF YOUR HAIR LONG BEFORE THEY CAN ARRIVE.
KSSSSSSH
I DON'T SAY ANYTHING. I FIGURE THAT'LL UNNERVE THEM EVEN MORE.
IRON MAN!

WIDE-BEAM, SHALLOW-EFFECT REPULSOR BLASTS TURN THE GLASS FRAGMENTS TO POWDER. DON'T WANT ANYONE GETTING HURT UNINTENTIONALLY.
KILL HIM!
BRATTATAT
BLAM
BLAM
BLAM
BRATTATAT
BUT MY DRAMATIC ENTRANCE -- AND MY SILENCE -- HAS THE DESIRED EFFECT.
THEY FOCUS ON ME.
SPANG
THE BULLETS SPEND THEMSELVES HARMLESSLY ON MY ARMOR, AND AN INERTIAL DAMPING FIELD PREVENTS RICOCHETS.
TING
SO BY THE TIME THEY THINK TO TAKE HOSTAGES --
BACK OFF, SIR GALAHAD -- OR WE SPLATTER THE LITTLE BROKERS ALL OVER YOUR SHINY TIN SUIT!

SENSORS WEAPONS COMM UTILS
REPULSOR
LASER
DECELERATIVE
CONCUSSIVE
PENETRATIVE
TARGET 1: LOCKED;
TARGET 2: LOCKED;
TARGET 3: LOCKED;
TARGET 4: _
-- I'VE GOT THEM ALL TARGETED.
WELL?
MOBILE TARGET LOCK - MULTIPLE
THE ARMOR DOES THE REST.
ZKAM
ZKAM
ZKAM
ZKAM
I DON'T LIKE DOING THIS, ORDINARILY. WHEN THE COMPUTERS TAKE OVER, I FEEL LIKE A PUPPET INSIDE THE ARMOR. BUT THERE ARE TIMES --
H-UHH!
UHH!
GHUH!
-- WHEN IT'S THE ONLY OPTION.
NO! I PLANNED THIS TO THE LAST SECOND! IT CAN'T HAVE GONE THIS WRONG -- THIS FAST!
NOT THIS FAST!
I'LL KILL YOU! KILL YOU!
I RECOGNIZE THE BODY ON THE FLOOR. IT'S GEORGIE. HE HAD AN EASY SMILE, UNRULY HAIR AND A DUMB JOKE FOR EVERY OCCASION.
FELLA --

NOT ANY MORE.
KRAMM
-- I THINK YOU'VE DONE ENOUGH.
AFTER THAT, IT'S ONLY A MATTER OF SWITCHING THE ELEVATORS BACK ON, AND LETTING THE POLICE TAKE OVER.
-- EXPRESS OUR DEEPEST THANKS FOR YOUR ASSISTANCE, IRON MAN.
I'M ONLY SORRY I COULDN'T HAVE ARRIVED EARLIER, MS. DENTON. GEORGE AVALON WAS A GOOD MAN.
THEY TREAT YOU LIKE A HERO, BODYGUARD -- BUT YOU'RE NO HERO! TONY STARK HAD MILLIONS INVESTED IN THIS PLACE --
-- AND HIS MERCENARY DOG WAS JUST PROTECTING HIS MASTER'S MONEY!
SWAT
SWAT
WELL, YOU HAVEN'T HEARD THE LAST OF ME! YOU'LL REGRET THE DAY YOU EVER MET VITTORIO SILVANI.
PTUI
IRON MAN!
I WON'T HOLD MY BREATH, MR. SILVANI. IN THE MEANTIME, I HOPE YOU FIND JAIL AN INTENSELY UNPLEASANT EXPERIENCE.
NOW, IF EVERYONE WILL EXCUSE ME --

"--I HAVE PLACES TO BE."
STARK TOWER.
STARK
SIXTY-SEVEN STORIES OF RETAIL SHOPS, OFFICES AND LUXURY APARTMENTS --
-- TOPPED OFF WITH A PENTHOUSE LEVEL AND ROOF GARDEN THAT'D MAKE THE RICHEST OF MIDDLE EASTERN OIL SHEIKS GREEN WITH ENVY.
I SHOULD KNOW. I OUTBID HIM FOR IT. BUT FOR ALL THAT IT'S A BIT OSTENTATIOUS...
...IT'S A PERFECT PLACE FOR A PARTY.
JAMESON. AND MY WIFE, DR. MARLA MADISON.
OF COURSE, SIR. I RECOGNIZE YOU FROM YOUR TELEVISION APPEARANCES.
JONAH! MARLA! SO GLAD YOU COULD MAKE IT!
HRMPH! USELESS, CODDLED POPINJAY!
OH, HUSH, JONAH. YOU KNOW YOU LOVE THIS!
I SEE YOU'VE ALREADY GOT YOUR NAME UP ON THE BUILDING.
WELL, WE WANTED EVERYTHING IN PLACE FOR THE RECHRISTENING PARTY -- IF IT'S GOING TO BE STARK TOWER, IT SHOULD SAY SO.
JONAH, MARLA, I'D LIKE TO PRESENT LEAH SHEFFIELD...
...SHE BROKERED THE SALE -- AND SHE'LL BE TAKING GUESTS AROUND ON THE NICKEL TOUR IN A FEW MINUTES, IF YOU'D LIKE TO SEE THE PLACE.
WILL YOU BE COMING, TONY?
NOT THIS TIME, LEAH --

"--I'D BETTER STAY HERE AND MINGLE."
FIVE HUNDRED AND SEVENTY OF NEW YORK'S BRIGHTEST LUMINARIES. I MOVE THROUGH THE ROOMS, SHAKING HANDS AND CHATTING.
THERE ARE A LOT OF PEOPLE TO REESTABLISH CONTACT WITH, A SURPRISING NUMBER OF WHOM I'M ACTUALLY GLAD TO SEE --
REED, SUE -- NICE TO SEE YOU. BEN AND JOHNNY COULDN'T MAKE IT?
OH, YOU KNOW BEN. HE MUTTERED SOMETHING ABOUT HOW HE'D RATHER HAVE PAINFUL EYE SURGERY. AND JOHNNY HAD A DATE.
NO ILL EFFECTS FROM YOUR INCARCERATION?
THE DOCTORS SAY I'M FIT AS A FIDDLE. AND YOU -- AFTER YOUR EXTRADIMENSIONAL ADVENTURE?
BUT AT THE SAME TIME. I CAN'T HELP BUT STEP BACK AND WATCH -- IT'S THE EXECUTIVE IN ME, I SUPPOSE.
THE VOLUME OF THE MUSIC, THE VENTILATION, THE WAITERS WITH THEIR CANAPÉS AND DRINKS -- IT ALL GOES VERY SMOOTHLY.
I'LL HAVE TO MAKE SURE THE CATERER GETS A NICE BONUS.
CHAMPAGNE, SIR?
YOU HAVE PELLEGRINO WATER BACK AT THE BAR, RIGHT?
I'LL GET YOU SOME RIGHT AWAY, SIR.
WELL, WELL -- IT'S THE MAN OF THE HOUR!
HM?

ROSALIND SHARPE AND FOGGY NELSON! REALLY, IT'S YOU TWO LEGAL EAGLES WHO DESERVE ALL THE APPLAUSE.
I'M STILL AMAZED AT THE PAINSTAKING WORK FOGGY DID ON MY PROBATE COURT CASE.
OH, IT WAS NOTHING, HONESTLY.
NO, I MEAN IT. YOUR COMMAND OF LEGAL HISTORY -- WHY, I HAD NO IDEA THERE WERE SO MANY PRECEDENTS, SO MANY BACK-TO-LIFE CASES.
WELL, THEY MOSTLY INVOLVE SUPER-VILLAINS, BUT STILL, THERE ARE A LOT OF --
AHEM. I'M SURE YOU'VE GOT OTHERS TO GREET, TONY, BUT I DID WANT TO LET YOU KNOW THAT THE FIRM WOULD BE INTERESTED -- VERY INTERESTED --
-- IN HELPING YOU OVERTURN THE FUJIKAWA SALE. WE'RE READY TO GO AS SOON AS YOU GIVE THE WORD.
AND I COULDN'T HAVE BETTER LAWYERS IN MY CORNER, MS. SHARPE. I APPRECIATE THE OFFER MORE THAN I CAN SAY.
BUT REALLY, I HAVEN'T DECIDED YET. I'LL LET YOU KNOW.
EVERYBODY'S GOT ADVICE FOR ME --
-- FROM NORMAN OSBORN OF OSBORN CHEMICAL --
YOU'VE GOT TO TAKE BACK WHAT'S YOURS, TONY. THAT'S THE ONLY WAY TO DO IT. YOU DON'T WANT TO LOOK WEAK, DO YOU?
-- TO SUNSET BAIN --
-- AND OF COURSE, BAINTRONICS WOULD LOVE TO WORK... CLOSELY WITH YOU -- PERHAPS A BRAND-NEW VENTURE, A PARTNERSHIP --
-- AND THEN THERE ARE THE CONGRATULATORY TELEGRAMS FROM THOSE WHO COULDN'T MAKE IT -- BETHANY CABE, MRS. ARBOGAST, JERRY SEINFELD --
(I REALLY HAVE TO DROP HIM A NOTE ABOUT THAT UNDERWEAR THING...)

AND THEN, OF COURSE, THERE'S THE UNALLOYED PLEASURE OF REUNITING WITH OLD FRIENDS...
PEPPER, RHODEY... I NEVER DID GET TO THANK YOU FOR ACTING AS TRUSTEES FOR MY ESTATE.
THAT'S THE WAY IT WORKS, DOESN'T IT? I MEAN, FOR MOST PEOPLE.
I SUPPOSE YOU'RE RIGHT. STILL, IT COULDN'T HAVE BEEN EASY FOR YOU...
AFTER ALL THE TIME WE WORKED FOR YOU, TONY? WE WERE HONORED. NOT THAT WE'RE IN A RUSH TO DO IT AGAIN OR ANYTHING...
ONE THING, THOUGH -- YOU'RE GETTING BETTER AT THIS. NUMBER A'TIMES YOU BEEN "DEAD", YOU MUST HAVE MORE LIVES THAN A CAT --
-- AN' THE WAY THIS WENT DOWN, I CAN'T EVEN BE MAD AT YOU FOR TURNIN' UP ALIVE AGAIN!
HA!
YEP -- NOT MY FAULT, NOT THIS TIME! AND I PROMISE -- NO MORE DYING FOR ME, NOT IF I CAN HELP IT!
BUT PEPPER -- WHERE'S THAT BROKEN-DOWN HUSBAND OF YOURS? COULDN'T HAPPY COME, OR--?
WELL, AH--
SAY, TONY --
-- DID I TELL YOU ABOUT MY NEW BUSINESS?
NEW BUSINESS?
YEAH -- RHODES RECOVERY. WE DO MARINE SALVAGE, AN' LIKE THAT.
YOU KINDA RUINED ME FOR THE EMPLOYEE LIFE, BUT I DON'T MUCH LIKE BOARDROOMS, EITHER. THIS WAY, I GET TO BE OUT IN THE OPEN AIR.
DROP IN, IF YOU'RE EVER DOWN ON THE GULF COAST.
AND THERE'S A TENTATIVE COUGH BEHIND ME --

TONY, M'BOY -- A WORD WITH YOU, IF I MIGHT?
I KNOW WHO IT IS BEFORE I EVEN TURN AROUND.
MY COUSIN MORGAN. THE BLACK SHEEP OF THE FAMILY. HE'S NOT USUALLY ANY TROUBLE, HIMSELF -- BUT IT TRAVELS WITH HIM.
THE CANE'S NEW, ISN'T IT?
A MINOR ACCIDENT -- I'M STILL RECOVERING. NOTHING TO WORRY ABOUT.
AH, TONY --
--I DON'T KNOW IF YOU'VE HEARD, BUT FUJIKAWA'S JUST MADE ME HEAD OF NORTH AMERICAN OPERATIONS. OF THE STARK COMPANIES.
I SUPPOSE THEY WANTED A STARK AT THE HELM, ONE WAY OR ANOTHER. BUT, WELL -- I KNOW YOU'RE THINKING OF CHALLENGING THE SALE --
-- BUT THIS IS A MAJOR OPPORTUNITY FOR ME, AND I'D, AH, CONSIDER IT A PERSONAL FAVOR IF YOU DIDN'T... UPSET THE APPLECART, AS IT WERE.
I'LL THINK ABOUT IT, MORGAN.
REALLY, I KNOW IT'S A BIG THING TO ASK, BUT --
I SAID I'LL THINK ABOUT IT. NOW, IF YOU'LL EXCUSE ME...
SOMETIMES IT SEEMS LIKE EVERYONE KNOWS EXACTLY WHAT I SHOULD DO -- AND IT'S WHATEVER'S IN THEIR BEST INTERESTS.
NOTHING NEW ABOUT THAT, OF COURSE. IT'S BEEN HAPPENING MY WHOLE LIFE.
USUALLY, I CAN JUST SHRUG IT OFF. FIGURE OUT WHAT I THINK IS BEST, AND DO THAT. THE TROUBLE IS, I DON'T KNOW WHAT'S BEST, NOT THIS TIME.
I DON'T KNOW WHAT I SHOULD DO...

I GUESS I STAY OUT ON THE BALCONY TOO LONG, BECAUSE EVENTUALLY...
EVERYONE'S GONE, TONY. IT WAS A WONDERFUL PARTY.
UNTIL THE HOST ZONED OUT AND VANISHED, EH?
THEY UNDERSTAND. YOU'VE BEEN THROUGH A LOT.
I'M JUST DISAPPOINTED --
-- AFTER ALL, YOU NEVER CAME ON ONE OF THE TOURS.
WELL, I LIVE HERE, AFTER ALL. I'VE SEEN IT.
I THOUGHT MAYBE I'D GIVE YOU A SPECIAL, PRIVATE TOUR...
...CONCENTRATING ON THE BEDROOMS...
I'M FLATTERED, LEAH, AND I'M SURE I'M BEING AN IDIOT TO SAY NO --
-- BUT I'M IN THE MOOD FOR SOLITUDE RIGHT NOW.
I'VE GOT A LOT TO THINK ABOUT.
WELL, IF YOU EVER CHANGE YOUR MIND...
...YOU'VE GOT MY NUMBER...

THAT I DO, LEAH -- AND IT'S TEMPTING, IT REALLY IS. JUST TO JUMP INTO BED WITH YOU AND FORGET EVERYTHING ELSE.
BUT IT SEEMS LIKE I'VE SPENT MY ENTIRE ADULT LIFE JUST REACTING TO EVENTS, REELING FROM CRISIS TO CRISIS --
-- EITHER CHARGING BLINDLY INTO THINGS, OR RUNNING AWAY, DISTRACTING MYSELF WITH WOMEN, WITH WORK, WITH ALCOHOL.
IT SEEMS LIKE I'VE NEVER REALLY HAD TIME TO THINK --
-- NOT SINCE THE VERY BEGINNING. I WAS SO YOUNG THEN -- IN SO MANY WAYS.
I THOUGHT ANY PROBLEM COULD BE SOLVED WITH BLUEPRINTS, FLOWCHARTS AND THE RIGHT NEW MANUFACTURING SYSTEMS --
-- AND THAT'S WHY I WAS THERE, AT MY SOUTHEAST ASIA PLANT, WHERE WE'D BEEN LOSING SUPPLIES TO A GUERRILLA LEADER NAMED WONG CHU.
MY PLANT MANAGER, TOSHIRO KANADA, THOUGHT THE ANSWER WAS MORE SECURITY -- AND I THOUGHT HE WAS BEING ALARMIST.
BUT THEN WE WERE ATTACKED --
WONG'S MEN!
HOW IN BLAZES DID THEY GET PAST THE OUTER PERIMETER?
WORRY ABOUT THAT LATER, MY FRIEND. GET TO COVER!
WE FLED INTO THE JUNGLE --
-- BUT UNFORTUNATELY --
SNIC
-- WONG CHU HAD LAID BOOBY TRAPS.
BOOM
KANADA WAS KILLED. AND I WAS BADLY INJURED -- A PIECE OF SHRAPNEL LODGED NEAR MY HEART. IT COULD HAVE KILLED ME AT ANY MOMENT --

-- BUT WONG CHU HAD PLANS FOR ME, BEFORE MY DEATH.
YOU WILL DESIGN WEAPONS -- FOR ME! AND IF YOUR WORK PLEASES ME, I WILL HAVE MY SURGEON SAVE YOUR WORTHLESS LIFE!
HE WAS LYING, AND WE BOTH KNEW IT --
-- BUT AT LEAST I HAD A CHANCE. WORKING WITH HO YINSEN, A BRILLIANT PHYSICIST AND ANOTHER PRISONER OF WONG'S --
-- WE CREATED THE SUIT OF ARMOR THAT WOULD KEEP MY HEART BEATING, THAT WOULD SAVE MY LIFE --
-- AND THAT WOULD GIVE ME THE POWER TO MAKE WONG CHU PAY -- FOR THE CRIMES HE'D COMMITTED, THE DEATHS HE'D CAUSED.
NO! YOU ARE NOT HUMAN!
BUT THAT WASN'T THE END OF IT.
IN THE YEARS SINCE, I RE-DESIGNED AND RE-BUILT MY ARMOR MANY TIMES, BECOMING AS FAMOUS AS IRON MAN AS I WAS AS TONY STARK.
EVEN WHEN MY HEART WAS REPAIRED, WHEN I DIDN'T NEED TO WEAR THE ARMOR ANY MORE, I KEPT WEARING IT --
-- THROUGH REFLEX MORE THAN ANY-THING ELSE.
I HAD THE BEST OF INTENTIONS, AND SO LITTLE EXPERIENCE. I WAS JUST TRYING TO MAKE A DIFFERENCE, AS BEST I COULD --

-- AND EVEN TODAY, LOOKING BACK ON IT ALL, I DON'T KNOW IF IT WAS THE RIGHT CHOICE.
IT'S FUNNY. THEY USED TO CALL ME "THE COOL EXEC WITH THE HEART OF STEEL," BUT THAT WAS AS MUCH A MASK AS IRON MAN'S FACEPLATE.
IF I TRY TO OVERTURN THE FUJIKAWA SALE, THEY'LL FIGHT BACK. I COULD PROBABLY WIN, BUT IT'D BE A LONG AND EXHAUSTING PROCESS --
-- AND I DON'T WANT TO DO IT JUST BECAUSE IT'S EXPECTED OF ME -- BECAUSE IT'S BEHAVIOR THAT FITS THE MASK.
I LOOK OUT AT THE CITY, AND MY THOUGHTS GO AROUND AGAIN. AND ABRUPTLY --
-- I WANT TO BE DOWN THERE.
I WANT TO BE A PART OF IT, NOT UP ABOVE, WATCHING FROM AN IVORY TOWER.
SHALL I CALL YOU A CAB, MR. STARK?
NO, KENDRICKS -- I THINK I'D RATHER WALK. BUT THANKS.
THE BRIEFCASE COMES WITH ME. THE BRIEFCASE ALWAYS COMES WITH ME.
PRINCE CHARMING HAS LEFT THE CASTLE. I REPEAT, PRINCE CHARMING HAS LEFT THE CASTLE. NO EVIDENT PROTECTION. I'M SHADOWING.
JKW
I WANDER AIMLESSLY. BUT UNSURPRISINGLY, I END UP --
-- AT THE CONSTRUCTION SITE.
-- TAKE A LOOK AROUND? SURE, I DON'T SEE ANY HARM IN THAT, SIR.
I THINK IT'S A WONDERFUL THING YOU AND THE FOUNDATION ARE DOING HERE.
THANKS... BILL, ISN'T IT?
NOW THERE'S A GOOD MAN. THE WORLD NEEDS MORE LIKE -- EH?
WHO ARE YOU? WHAT'S YOUR BUSINESS HERE?
IN A COUPLE OF SECONDS, FRIEND --

-- YOU WON'T CARE.
THE MINUTE I'M INSIDE THE STRUCTURE, I START TO FEEL BETTER.
THIS IS WHAT IT'S REALLY ALL ABOUT.
STEEL AND RIVETS. WOOD AND PLASTER. THE SKELETON OF SOMETHING THAT'S SLOWLY COMING TO LIFE --
-- SOMETHING THAT'LL MAKE PEOPLE'S LIVES BETTER.
IT'S ABOUT BUILDING, ABOUT IMPROVING. AND AFTER ALL THE WORLD'S BEEN THROUGH RECENTLY, ALL THE DAMAGE IT'S SEEN --
-- IT NEEDS THIS. AND MORE.
I'M BREATHING IN THE SAWDUST AND THE SMELL OF CONSTRUCTION, AND THINKING THAT THIS IS THE KIND OF THING I SHOULD BE DOING --
-- WHEN --
BRAT TAT VIT TAT VIT
WHA --? GUNFIRE?
BUT -- WHO --?
GOOD EVENING, ANTHONY STARK.
NICE NIGHT, ISN'T IT?

ALLOW ME TO INTRODUCE MY COMPANIONS AND MYSELF. I'M FIREFIGHT --
-- AND BEHIND ME ARE ROCKET-LAUNCHER, AIRBORNE, SMOKESCREEN AND BOOBYTRAP.
TOGETHER, WE'RE THE
DEATH SQUAD.
DON'T BOTHER RACKING YOUR BRAIN -- WE HAVEN'T MET. NOT AT ANY OF YOUR FANCY PARTIES OR IN ANY EXECUTIVE WASHROOMS.
BUT SOMEONE WANTS YOU DEAD -- AND WE'VE BEEN HIRED TO DO THE JOB.
SOMEONE? SOMEONE LIKE FUJIKAWA, MAYBE?
AH-AH. IT'D BE A VIOLATION OF PROFESSIONAL ETHICS TO NAME OUR EMPLOYER. I'M SURE YOU UNDERSTAND.
STILL, I'D LIKE TO THANK YOU FOR LEAVING YOUR BUILDING LIKE THAT --

-- IT'S MADE THIS MUCH EASIER THAN I THOUGHT IT WOULD BE.
GOODBYE, MR. STARK.
SECONDS AGO, MY HEAD WAS FULL OF ENGINEERING PRINCIPLES -- STRESS, LOAD-BEARING STRUCTURES, HYDRAULICS AND SO ON.
NOW, THE ONLY ONE I CAN THINK OF --
-- IS THE LEVER!
TUNK
KLATTA
KATTL
WH--
AAAGH!
I KNOW I'VE ONLY BOUGHT MYSELF SECONDS, SO I DON'T HESITATE -- I DIVE FOR THE INTERIOR OF THE STRUCTURE, FOR THE SHADOWS --
-- AND, BEHIND ME --
WELL. SO MUCH FOR ETIQUETTE. GENTLEMEN AND LADIES --
-- YOU ARE CLEARED TO ENGAGE!

CHOOM
I DON'T LIKE THIS MUCH.
I RUN FOR ALL I'M WORTH, ZIGGING AND ZAGGING LIKE I'M STILL TAILBACK ON MY COLLEGE FOOTBALL TEAM --
SPWEE
BRAC
BRATAT
-- AND WHILE THAT KEEPS ME IN ONE PIECE, AT LEAST FOR THE MOMENT --
-- THE FLOOR IN FRONT OF ME DOESN'T ENJOY THE SAME GOOD FORTUNE.
WHOA!
UUHH!
I LAND PAINFULLY --
-- AND MY RIBS ARE GOING TO LET ME REMEMBER THE FEELING FOR DAYS -- IF I LIVE THAT LONG.
BUT AT LEAST THIS GIVES ME A FEW MORE MOMENTS. AND IF THAT LETS ME FIND SOME COVER --

-- THOSE FEW MOMENTS WILL BE ALL I NEED.
WHMP
MOVE, MOVE!
HE'S ONLY ONE MAN! ONE UNARMED MAN! FAN OUT AND FIND HIM! THE NEXT TIME I SEE THIS GUY--
-- I WANT HIM TO BE A CONFIRMED KILL!
SMOKE-SCREEN! I WANT HEAT READINGS -- NOW!
YESSIR, FIREFIGHT. I'M SCANNING.
GOT ANY-THING?
SOMETHING -- BUT I DON'T THINK IT'S HIM. READINGS ARE KINDA WEIRD. WHAT-EVER IT IS, THOUGH, IT'S MOBILE --
-- AND IT'S BEHIND US.
MR. STARK HAD TO GO -- BUT HE LEFT A MESSAGE FOR YOU.
HE ASKED ME TO TELL YOU HE'S UNABLE TO MEET YOU RIGHT NOW --

-- BUT MAYBE I CAN HELP YOU INSTEAD.
IT'S GRATIFYING TO HEAR THEM GASP. I GUESS THEY'RE NOT QUITE AS COLD AND HARDENED AS THEY LIKE TO THINK.
STILL, THEY'RE VERY GOOD.
THEY RECOVER QUICKLY, AND BRING THEIR WEAPONS TO BEAR -- PLANNING TO TAKE ME DOWN BEFORE I CAN GET CLOSER.

I DON'T GIVE THEM THE CHANCE.
UHH!
KKRAKK
ALL RIGHT. NOW THAT WE'RE ALL HERE, WE SHOULD GET A FEW GROUND RULES STRAIGHT.
FIRST, YOU'RE A BUNCH OF JUMPED-UP PUNKS WITH HI-TECH ORDNANCE YOU GOT OUT OF A CRACKERJACK BOX SOMEWHERE.
SECOND, I'M IRON MAN.
THIRD --
KRABSH
-- NO, I GUESS THOSE TWO PRETTY WELL COVER IT.
NOW -- YOU'VE GOT ABOUT THREE SECONDS TO TELL ME WHO HIRED YOU, OR TRUST ME, YOU'LL REGRET STAYING SILENT --
'LAUNCHER! PEST CONTROL!

GOTCHA, BOSS!
WH --?
KROOM
NICE MOVE.
I DIDN'T THINK HE'D RISK IT, THAT CLOSE TO FIREFIGHT. BUT HE'S GOOD ENOUGH TO PULL IT OFF, AND TO ANGLE HIS SHOT FOR MAXIMUM DAMAGE.
WHAM
SCORE ONE FOR THEM.
SHRMBBPH
I NEED SPACE -- MANEUVERABILITY. IN AN ENCLOSED AREA LIKE THIS THEY'VE GOT TOO MUCH OF AN ADVANTAGE.
I HEAD FOR OPEN AIR, EXPECTING THEY'LL FOLLOW.
BUT --
AIRBORNE! FETCH!
UH-OH.
SHE'S FASTER THAN I AM, AND SHE STUNTS AROUND LIKE SHE WAS BORN IN THE SKY.
BRAM BRAM BRAM
I'M HEADED BACK DOWNWARD BEFORE I EVEN KNOW IT.

AND AS MY GYROS START RIGHTING ME, GETTING ME BACK IN CONTROL --
KSH
MY BOOT-JETS!
KSSH
SOME SORT OF VISCOUS COMPOUNDS, GUMMING THEM UP. I'M GROUNDED. SCORE TWO FOR THEM.
THEY'VE HAD THE MOMENTUM SO FAR. TIME TO REVERSE THAT.
ALL RIGHT, MOVE IN. WE'LL MAKE HIM TELL US WHERE HIS BOSS IS.
I ENGAGE TARGETING, AND SCAN FOR THEM. I'VE GOT FIREFIGHT, BOOBYTRAP AND AIRBORNE IN FRONT, ROCKETLAUNCHER BEHIND.
NO SIGN OF SMOKESCREEN -- MAYBE I PUT HER DOWN IN THAT FIRST ATTACK?
DEATHSQUAD! HE'S GOT YOU IN TARGET LOCK --
-- BUT NOT FOR LONG!
PAFF
BLAST -- SHE MUST BE CLOAKED SOMEHOW! SHE GOT CLOSE TO ME -- FILLED THE AIR WITH SOME SORT OF METAL FOIL --
-- AND NOW ALL MY SENSORS REGISTER IS SNOW.
OKAY, THAT'S THREE. YOU DON'T GET ANY MORE. YOU WANT TO DO THIS THE HARD WAY --
-- THAT'S JUST FINE WITH ME.

THE GROUND SHIFTS BEHIND ME. TOO HEAVY TO BE ANYONE BUT ROCKETLAUNCHER --
ZKAM
-- AND WHAT DO YOU KNOW, I'M RIGHT.
A DOUBLE REPULSOR BLAST PUTS HIM DOWN.
AND THEN IT'S AIRBORNE'S TURN.
I LET HER THINK HER MISSILES STAND A CHANCE --
-- AND THEN SHE'S IN POSITION, SO I SIDESTEP, AND --
WH--?
ZKAM
KROOM
UUGH!
MY ARMOR COULD TAKE THAT, BUT SHE SACRIFICED DEFENSE FOR SPEED. THAT'S THE WAY IT GOES.

NEXT?
BRAK KAK KAK
REMEMBER, BOOBYTRAP --
-- HE'S GROUNDED -- HE CAN'T ZIP AROUND LIKE HE USUALLY DOES. SO I'LL GET HIS ATTENTION --
-- WHILE YOU TAKE HIM APART FROM THE FEET UP.
I'M SORRY --
-- BUT YOU MUST HAVE ME CONFUSED WITH MY BOSS.
SPANG
TING
PING
MR. STARK, HE'S GOT TO BE SLICK AND SMART, WALTZ HIS WAY THROUGH ALL THOSE CORPORATE MINE-FIELDS --
-- BUT IRON MAN DOESN'T HAVE TO TIPTOE THROUGH MINE-FIELDS -- I JUST ROLL RIGHT THROUGH 'EM!
I HEAR MYSELF SAY IT, AND I WONDER -- IS THAT ONE OF THE REASONS I KEEP DOING THIS? WHY I'VE NEVER QUIT BEING IRON MAN FOR LONG?
BUT I PUT IT ASIDE -- I CAN THINK ABOUT IT LATER. RIGHT NOW, I'VE GOT WORK TO DO. I RAISE MY HAND FOR A REPULSOR BLAST --
CHOOM
-- AND --
SMOKESCREEN --

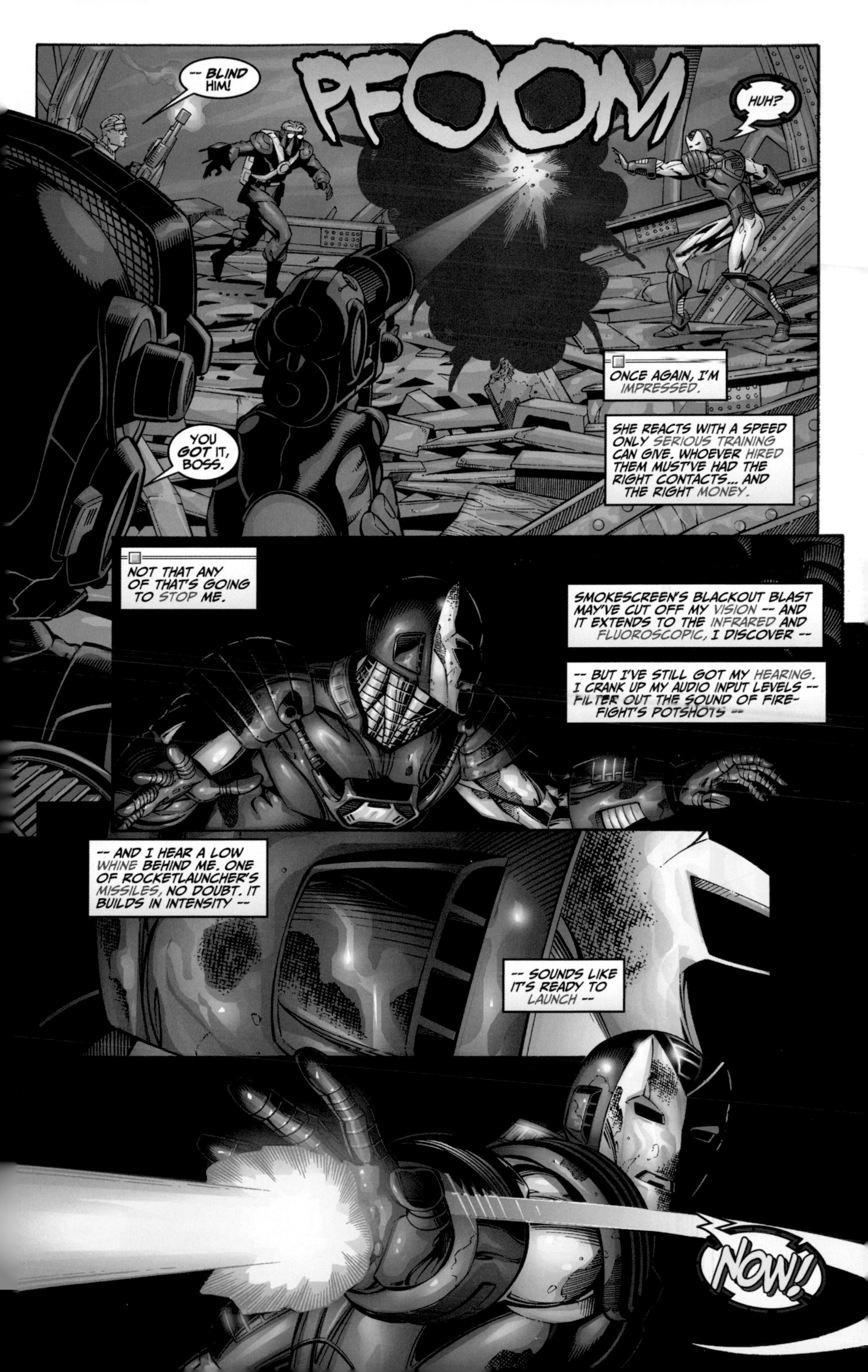
-- BLIND HIM!
PFOOM
HUH?
YOU GOT IT, BOSS.
ONCE AGAIN, I'M IMPRESSED.
SHE REACTS WITH A SPEED ONLY SERIOUS TRAINING CAN GIVE. WHOEVER HIRED THEM MUST'VE HAD THE RIGHT CONTACTS... AND THE RIGHT MONEY.
NOT THAT ANY OF THAT'S GOING TO STOP ME.
SMOKESCREEN'S BLACKOUT BLAST MAY'VE CUT OFF MY VISION -- AND IT EXTENDS TO THE INFRARED AND FLUOROSCOPIC, I DISCOVER --
-- BUT I'VE STILL GOT MY HEARING. I CRANK UP MY AUDIO INPUT LEVELS -- FILTER OUT THE SOUND OF FIRE-FIGHT'S POTSHOTS --
-- AND I HEAR A LOW WHINE BEHIND ME. ONE OF ROCKETLAUNCHER'S MISSILES, NO DOUBT. IT BUILDS IN INTENSITY --
-- SOUNDS LIKE IT'S READY TO LAUNCH --
NOW!!

KREKAKK
HUH?
KRUMMP!
FROM THE SOUND OF IT, THE BACKLASH SETS OFF ANOTHER MISSILE, MAYBE MORE. HE'S PRETTY TOUGH -- BUT THAT'LL SLOW HIM DOWN, AT LEAST.
STILL, I CAN'T REST ON MY LAURELS --
-- IF I WERE SMOKESCREEN, I'D BE LOOKING TO TAKE OUT ANOTHER OF MY SENSES. I CRANK UP MY HEARING FURTHER--
-- AND THERE SHE IS. MAYBE SHE CAN CLOAK HERSELF FROM ORDINARY DETECTION --
-- BUT I CAN STILL PICK UP HER HEART-BEAT. I REACH OUT --
-- AND, MOMENTS LATER....
I CAN KEEP THIS UP ALL NIGHT, FIREFIGHT. I DON'T THINK YOU CAN.
READY TO SURRENDER -- TO TELL ME WHO YOU'RE WORKING FOR?
NO. NO, I DON'T THINK SO. THERE'LL BE OTHER TIMES, IRON MAN --
-- AND OTHER CHANCES.

AIRBORNE! PICKUP!
BOOBYTRAP, 'LAUNCHER! EVAC -- NOW!
POOM POOM POOM
AND, ONCE AGAIN --
-- THEY'RE MOVING WHILE I'M STILL REACTING. WORKING AS A WELL-OILED, EFFICIENT TEAM --
-- AND LEAVING ME FEELING LIKE A DOPE, IMPOTENTLY TRIGGERING MY BOOT-JET CONTROL, AND GETTING NO RESPONSE.
YOU COME BACK ANY TIME YOU WANT, FIRE-FIGHT! BUT BEFORE YOU DO, TELL YOUR BOSS -- TONY STARK'S PROTECTED!
I'LL BE HERE WAITING FOR YOU -- I'LL ALWAYS BE HERE!
YOU HEAR ME?!
MY VOICE ECHOES, FLAT AND METALLIC, AND I REALIZE I'M SHOUTING TO NOBODY. THEY'RE GONE --
-- AND OFF IN THE DISTANCE, I HEAR THE FIRST SOUND OF SIRENS. AND THEN --
-- AND THEN --
OH, MY LORD.

-- I LOOK AROUND.
THIS WAS GOING TO BE A COMMUNITY CENTER. THERE WERE GOING TO BE MEDICAL FACILITIES ABOVE IT, AND LOW-COST HOUSING ABOVE THAT.
IT WAS DESPERATELY NEEDED BY THE PEOPLE OF THIS NEIGHBORHOOD.
AND NOW IT'S GONE. ALL THAT WORK, ALL THAT EFFORT, ALL THAT POTENTIAL -- REDUCED TO RUBBLE IN A MATTER OF MINUTES.
I WON THE BATTLE, I TELL MYSELF. BUT STACKED UP AGAINST THE COST -- THAT DOESN'T FEEL LIKE ANY KIND OF TRIUMPH.

ALL IT FEELS LIKE IS LOSS. AND I DON'T EVEN KNOW WHY IT HAPPENED.
SOME ENEMY FROM MY PAST. SOMEONE WHO WANTS ME DEAD. AND BETWEEN US, THAT UNRESOLVED HATRED --
-- DESTROYED A LOT OF INNOCENT PEOPLE'S HOPE FOR THE FUTURE.
I STAND THERE IN THE WRECKAGE FOR A LONG TIME. THE POLICE COME, THEY TAKE A STATEMENT, THEY GO. AND AFTER A WHILE --
-- AFTER A WHILE, I LEAVE TOO.

LATER, I TINKER WITH MY ARMOR -- CLEANING OUT THE BOOT-JETS, WORKING ON SOME IDEAS TO IMPROVE MY SENSOR SYSTEM.
ORDINARILY, I LOVE THIS. THE PRIVATE ACCESS TO THIS BASEMENT LAB WAS ONE OF THE REASONS I BOUGHT THIS BUILDING. BUT TONIGHT --
-- IT JUST DOESN'T WORK.
IS THIS ALL MY LIFE COMES DOWN TO? FIGHTING BATTLES, LOSING GROUND ON THE THINGS THAT MATTER TO ME --
-- AND THEN MAKING REPAIRS SO I CAN DO IT AGAIN?
NO!
66
I SPEND THE REST OF THE NIGHT THINKING. WEIGHING MY OPTIONS.
TRYING, FOR ONCE, TO FIGURE OUT WHAT REALLY MATTERS TO ME. WHAT I WANT TO DO.
WHO I WANT TO BE.

AS DAWN STARTS TO BREAK, I MAKE A FEW DECISIONS.
AND THEN I MAKE A FEW PHONE CALLS.
ONE'S TO A PUBLIC RELATIONS FIRM I'VE USED IN THE PAST. THEY'RE AS GOOD IN THEIR WAY AS THE DEATHSQUAD, AND AS A RESULT --
-- REPORTERS FROM THE MAJOR NEWSPAPERS, MAGAZINES, NETWORKS AND MORE ARE CONGREGATING AT STARK TOWER WITHIN FOUR HOURS.
WHADDAYA THINK -- FUJIKAWA?
GOT TO BE. WHAT ELSE?
-- LAWYERS WORKING LIKE MAD, GETTING SOMETHING FINISHED --
-- NOTHING AT THE COURTHOUSE, THOUGH, NOT YET --
GOOD MORNING. I'D LIKE TO THANK YOU ALL FOR COMING, ESPECIALLY ON SUCH SHORT NOTICE. AND I DO HAVE AN ANNOUNCEMENT --
-- THOUGH PERHAPS NOT THE ONE YOU'RE EXPECTING. I WILL NOT BE TRYING TO TAKE STARK ENTERPRISES BACK FROM FUJIKAWA.
AFTER ONSLAUGHT, AFTER THE DIVISIVENESS OF THE LATEST ANTI-MUTANT WITCH-HUNT, AFTER ALL THE WORLD'S BEEN THROUGH RECENTLY --
-- WE NEED POSITIVE ACTION. WE NEED TO BE WORKING TOWARD RECONSTRUCTION, NOT ARGUING OVER SCRAPS.
A LENGTHY COURT BATTLE, AT THIS TIME, WOULD JUST BE A COSTLY DISTRACTION THAT WOULDN'T BENEFIT ANYONE.
INSTEAD --
STARK SOLUTIONS
-- I'M ANNOUNCING THE FORMATION OF A NEW CONSULTING COMPANY -- STARK SOLUTIONS. WHATEVER YOUR PROBLEM -- WE CAN HELP FIX IT.
MY SERVICES WILL BE AVAILABLE TO BUSINESS, TO GOVERNMENT, TO PRIVATE INDIVIDUALS, TO ANYONE -- WITH ONE SMALL HITCH.

I DON'T COME CHEAP. MY FEES WILL BE AS HIGH AS THE CALIBER OF MY WORK --
-- AND I DON'T THINK I'M BEING IMMODEST WHEN I SAY THAT'S VERY HIGH INDEED. BUT THE MONEY WON'T BE GOING TO LINE MY POCKETS.
NO, THE MONEY STARK SOLUTIONS WILL BRING IN WILL LARGELY BE TURNED OVER TO THE MARIA STARK FOUNDATION FOR RECONSTRUCTION PROJECTS --
-- FOR PROJECTS THAT'LL HELP MAKE THE WORLD A BETTER PLACE. I WANT TO LOOK TO THE FUTURE, NOT THE PAST. TO BUILD, RATHER THAN DESTROY.
AND THAT SAID --
-- THERE'S ONLY ONE OTHER PERSON TO HEAR FROM.
STARK SOLUTIONS
KLIK
HI.
DURING HIS YEARS IN BUSINESS, AND HIS ASSOCIATION WITH ME AND WITH THE AVENGERS, MR. STARK HAS MADE A NUMBER OF ENEMIES.
HE'S CHOOSING TO IGNORE THEM. I'M NOT.
SO IF ANY OF YOU OUT THERE THINK THAT THIS NEW VENTURE MEANS THAT MR. STARK'S GONE SOFT, THAT HE'S LEFT HIMSELF UN-PROTECTED --
-- THINK AGAIN.
YOU WANT TO COME AFTER MR. STARK -- YOU WANT TO HURT HIM, KILL HIM, STOP HIM FROM DOING WHAT HE'S SETTING OUT TO DO --
-- YOU DO IT OVER IRON MAN'S DEAD BODY. THAT'S ALL I'VE GOT TO SAY.
THE SCREEN GOES BLANK --

-- AND THE ROOM ERUPTS WITH SOUND.
MR. STARK!
DO YOU INTEND TO--
OVER HERE!
MR. STARK!
DOES THIS MEAN THAT--
I JUST LISTEN TO IT FOR A MOMENT, LET IT WASH OVER ME. IT FEELS GOOD, WHAT I'M DOING. IT FEELS RIGHT.
I'M HOPING A PUBLIC DECLARATION OF DISINTEREST IN OLD ENMITIES WILL MAKE WHOEVER SENT THE DEATHSQUAD BACK OFF. BUT IT'S NOT LIKELY.
A TINY, UNPROTECTED COMPANY, DEFENSELESS EXCEPT FOR IRON MAN?
I MIGHT AS WELL JUST PAINT A TARGET ON MY BACK.
BUT THAT'S GOOD, TOO. IT'LL FLUSH THEM OUT INTO THE OPEN --
-- AND LET IRON MAN DEAL WITH THEM. AND TONY STARK'LL JUST GET ON WITH HIS LIFE --
-- AND THE WORK HE WANTS TO DO.
YES, COKIE. YOU HAVE A QUESTION?
AND I KNOW THAT AROUND THE WORLD, THERE'LL BE REACTIONS TO MY LITTLE ANNOUNCEMENT --
STARK FUJIKAWA
SEEMS LIKE GOOD NEWS.
YES, UNLESS HE'S PLAYING SOME DEEPER GAME.
WE HAD BETTER KEEP A CLOSE EYE ON MR. STARK...

-- AND I KNOW THAT WHETHER THEY REACT POSITIVELY OR NEGATIVELY --
I WANT A PROJECT THAT NEEDS TONY STARK'S ATTENTION.
I WANT SOME-THING WE CAN HIRE HIM FOR -- AND I WANT IT BY CLOSE OF BUSINESS TODAY. ONE WAY OR ANOTHER --
-- TONY STARK'S GOING TO END UP WORKING FOR ME.
-- WHETHER THEY WISH ME WELL OR ILL --
ANTHONY STARK IS TOO DANGEROUS TO REMAIN A FREE AGENT.
CONFINED TO ONE AREA, HE CAN BE PREDICTED. BUT LOOSE LIKE THIS --
-- HE MUST BE CONTAINED. OR DESTROYED.
-- I'M READY FOR THEM.
SO. MY BETRAYER NOT ONLY LIVES, HE THRIVES. THAT MUST BE REMEDIED...
WHOEVER THEY ARE, WHATEVER THEY DO, I'LL HANDLE IT.
THEY'RE NOT GOING TO STOP ME. THEY'RE NOT GOING TO DISTRACT ME.
ENJOY YOUR MOMENT IN THE SUN, STARK -- ENJOY IT WHILE YOU CAN! FOR I OWE YOU GREAT PAIN AND SUFFERING, AND I ASSURE YOU, SIR --
-- THAT DEBT WILL BE REPAID -- IN FULL!
I KNOW WHO I AM. I KNOW WHERE I'M GOING. AND THAT'S ALL THAT MATTERS.
WELL, WELL, WELL. THIS SHOULD PROVE MOST INTERESTING.
MOST INTERESTING INDEED..!

"HER NAME WAS LINDY.
"SHE WAS JUST A KID -- JUST FOURTEEN YEARS OLD, BUT SHE WAS INTO EVERYTHING. ONE WEEK, SHE'D WANNA BE A VET WHEN SHE GREW UP --
"-- AND THE NEXT, SHE WAS GONNA BE THE FIRST WOMAN ON MARS.
"BUT MOST OF ALL, IT SEEMED LIKE, WHAT SHE WANTED TO DO --
"-- WAS HANG OUT WITH HER OLDER BROTHER."
DON'T LOOK NOW, JOSTEN -- BUT HERE COMES YER KID SISTER AGAIN.
WHYN'TCHA TELL HER TO COME BACK IN A COUPLE YEARS -- WHEN SHE'S FILLED OUT SOME?
HEY, ERIK -- YOU GOIN' IN TO MADISON? CAN I COME?
FORGET IT, LIND. YOU'RE JUST NOT OLD ENOUGH -- OR TOUGH ENOUGH -- TO HANG WITH MY CROWD.
BEAT IT ON BACK TO YOUR DOLLS, WILLYA?

"I WAS SEVENTEEN, A WILD KID -- THE LAST THING I WANTED WAS TO BE SADDLED WITH A BABY SISTER. I DIDN'T KNOW HOW MUCH SHE LOOKED UP TO ME --
"-- OR HOW MUCH I WAS HURTIN' HER. BUT THAT NIGHT, AFTER WE TOOK OFF..."
"NOT TOUGH ENOUGH," Huh? I'LL SHOW YOU TOUGH ENOUGH...
"SHE TOOK OFF AFTER US ON HER BIKE -- LIKE SHE WAS GONNA BIKE ALL THE WAY INTO TOWN. IT WAS THIRTY MILES -- MORE, BY BACK ROADS --
"-- BUT SHE DIDN'T QUIT. IT GOT DARK, SHE GOT TIRED --
"-- THEY SAY SHE MUST'VE BEEN WAVERING ALL OVER THE ROAD.
"SO WHEN THE DRIVER CAME AROUND THAT BLIND CURVE..."
WELL, THEY SAID THERE WAS NO TIME FOR HIM TO BRAKE -- AN' NO CHANCE FOR HER.
SHE HELD ON 'TIL I GOT TO THE HOSPITAL, AN' THEN... THEN WE LOST HER.
IT WAS AFTER THAT I RAN OFF, JOINED THE ARMY -- AN' GRADUATED FROM JUVENILE DELINQUENCY TO SERIOUS TROUBLE.
I JUST...
CITY HA

... I GUESS I JUST DIDN'T WANT TO BE LOOKED UP TO ANYMORE. I DIDN'T WANT TO BE RESPONSIBLE FOR ANYONE OR ANYTHING --
-- OR AT LEAST, NOT FOR ANYTHING LIKE THAT.
I'M -- I'M SO SORRY, ATLAS. YOU DIDN'T HAVE TO TELL ME, REALLY. IT'S JUST -- YOU MENTIONED YOUR SISTER ONCE, AND I WAS CURIOUS...
IT'S OKAY, KID. I DON'T MIND YOU KNOWIN'. IT'S FUNNY -- IN A LOT OF WAYS, YOU REMIND ME OF HER.
GEEZ, IT WAS SO LONG AGO...
I CAN'T BELIEVE YOU GUYS ARE TALKING ABOUT THE PAST, NOT WITH EVERYTHING THAT'S HAPPENED, THE LAST FEW DAYS --
-- NOT WITH WHAT'S ABOUT TO HAPPEN! I MEAN, I DON'T KNOW ABOUT YOU, BUT MY HEART'S BEATING SO FAST, I COULD -- Huh?
SHOOM
SORRY I'M LATE, GANG. I HAD A FEW THINGS TO TAKE CARE OF. HOPE I HAVEN'T MISSED ANYTHING.
IS EVERYTHING SET, TECHNO?
EVERYTHING'S FINE, CITIZEN V --
TECHNO'S VOICE RINGS HOLLOWLY, WITH A PRONOUNCED ELECTRONIC BUZZ.
IT COULD BE THAT HE'S MISALIGNED HIS VOICE CIRCUITS, STILL NOT USED TO ALL THE INTRICACIES OF HIS ROBOTIC BODY[8]--
[8] WHICH HE GOT IN #7-8. – Tom
-- OR IT COULD BE THAT HE'S IN COMPLETE CONTROL OF HIS NEW FORM -- AND SIMPLY LIKES THE WAY IT SOUNDS.
-- EVERYTHING'S GOING LIKE CLOCKWORK.
THINGS ARE STARTING, THUNDERBOLTS -- WE'LL NEED YOU IN FIVE MINUTES!
THANKS, DALLAS.

AND, IN THE CONFERENCE CHAMBER...
FOR ME TO CALL THE LAST FEW DAYS MOMENTOUS WOULD BE QUITE AN UNDER-STATEMENT.
VIRTUALLY EVERY MAN, WOMAN AND CHILD ON EARTH --
-- HAS BEEN WITNESS TO AT LEAST A PART OF WHAT'S OCCURRED --
"-- STARTING WITH THE FANTASTIC LIGHT SHOW THAT RIPPED THROUGH THE SKIES OF OUR PLANET, A LIGHT-SHOW VISIBLE FROM EVERY CORNER OF THE GLOBE --
"-- AND WHICH HERALDED THE RETURN OF HEROES LONG THOUGHT LOST TO US, HEROES WHO'D BEEN PRESUMED DEAD."
"THE FANTASTIC FOUR WERE DISCOVERED IN UPSTATE NEW YORK --
"-- TELLING A TALE OF ANOTHER DIMENSION, AND AN INCREDIBLE CONFLICT THERE.
"BUT THOUGH THEY WERE THE FIRST TO REAPPEAR, THEY WERE FAR FROM THE LAST. CAPTAIN AMERICA HAS BEEN SEEN IN JAPAN --
"-- THE ANDROID VISION IN LONDON, GIANT-MAN AND THE WASP IN CAIRO, HAWKEYE IN PERTH -- AND OTHERS ARE STILL BEING DISCOVERED.
"AND OUR WORLD IS GRATEFUL FOR THE RETURN OF THESE NOBLE MEN AND WOMEN. BUT WE ARE HERE TODAY TO HONOR OTHER HEROES --"
-- HEROES WHO STEPPED INTO THE BREACH WHEN ALL SEEMED LOST, WHO ROSE TO THE OCCASION WHEN THEY WERE MOST NEEDED --
-- HEROES WHO DEFENDED US ALL THROUGH OUR LONG NIGHT. LADIES AND GENTLEMEN --

-- I GIVE YOU TECHNO, ATLAS, MACH-1, SONGBIRD, JOLT, CITIZEN V AND METEORITE. I GIVE YOU --
-- THE
THUNDERBOLTS!
THE APPLAUSE IS IMMEDIATE, ENTHUSIASTIC, HEARTFELT AND SUSTAINED -- AND THERE IS NO DOUBT, NONE WHATSOEVER, THAT IT IS WELL DESERVED.
NOT BAD...
A TITANIC TURNING POINT FOR MARVEL'S MIGHTIEST MISCREANTS!
HEROES' REWARD

AND THE THUNDERBOLTS GET MORE THAN JUST OUR GRATITUDE TODAY, MORE THAN OUR RESPECT.
I'M DELIGHTED TO ANNOUNCE THAT, AS OF NINE THIS MORNING --
-- THE NATIONAL SECURITY COUNCIL AND THE UNITED NATIONS GRANTED THE THUNDERBOLTS A PARAGON-LEVEL SECURITY CLEARANCE --
-- AND THEIR HEAD-QUARTERS COMPUTER SYSTEMS HAVE BEEN LINKED TO MILITARY, INTERPOL AND CIVILIAN ALERT SYSTEMS AROUND THE WORLD.
THIS IS THE SAME STATUS LONG ENJOYED BY BOTH THE AVENGERS AND THE FANTASTIC FOUR. AND THIS DEVELOPMENT, I HOPE --
-- WILL ALLOW THE THUNDERBOLTS TO DO AN EVEN BETTER JOB OF PROTECTING INNOCENTS. AND NOW, WITHOUT FURTHER ADO --
-- I YIELD THE FLOOR TO CITIZEN V.
-- AND EVEN JADED, CYNICAL REPORTERS FIND THEMSELVES CHEERING THEIR THROATS HOARSE.
THANK YOU, MR. MAYOR. I KNOW I SPEAK FOR MY ENTIRE TEAM --
-- WHEN I SAY THAT WE ARE HONORED BY THIS GESTURE ON THE WORLD'S PART, AND THE FAITH ITS PEOPLE HAVE PLACED IN US.
I CAN ONLY HOPE THAT WE WILL NEVER LOSE SIGHT OF THE GOALS AND IDEALS THAT HAVE LED US TO THIS POINT.
APPLAUSE ROLLS FORTH ONCE MORE, LOUDER AND LONGER THIS TIME --
CITIZEN V -- A QUESTION. WHEN YOU STARTED OUT, DID YOU HAVE ANY IDEA YOU'D BE SO SUCCESSFUL?
WE CERTAINLY HOPED FOR THE BEST, OF COURSE --
-- BUT WE HAD NO EXPECTATIONS, NOTHING BUT A DESIRE TO DO AS WELL AS WE COULD.

THERE HAS BEEN NO WORD AS TO WHETHER THE AVENGERS WILL BE REGROUPING --
-- DO YOU THINK THE THUNDERBOLTS HAVE TAKEN THEIR PLACE, THAT THERE'S NO NEED FOR THEM WITH YOU AROUND?
IF THE AVENGERS RE-FORM, IT'LL BE GOOD NEWS FOR THE ENTIRE WORLD. WE WOULD NEVER DREAM OF REPLACING THEM, EVEN IF THAT WERE POSSIBLE.
WHAT ABOUT THE FANTASTIC FOUR? NOW THAT THEY'RE BACK, WILL YOU BE KEEPING FOUR FREEDOMS PLAZA?
FOUR FREEDOMS PLAZA BELONGS TO THE FANTASTIC FOUR, AND IS ONLY ON LOAN TO US. THE MOMENT THEY WANT IT BACK --
-- IT'S THEIRS, UNCONDITIONALLY.
BUT EVEN AS CITIZEN V FINISHES SPEAKING, THERE'S A COMMOTION AT THE BACK OF THE ROOM, AND --
KSSSSSSHH
WHAT IN --? S.H.I.E.L.D. AGENTS?
CITIZEN V -- A.K.A HELMUT ZEMO -- YOU AND THE REST OF THE THUNDERBOLTS ARE UNDER ARREST --
-- FOR YOUR CRIMES AS THE MASTERS OF EVIL!
FOR A MOMENT, THERE'S NOTHING BUT STUNNED SILENCE.

THEN...
THE -- THE MASTERS OF --?
THE MASTERS OF EVIL?
ZAK ZAK
TECHNO! AS WE DISCUSSED --
--NOW!
D-DID HE SAY "ZEMO"?
TECHNO CONCENTRATES. WITHIN HIS MECHANICAL BODY, SWITCHES CONNECT, CIRCUITS ACTIVATE --
-- AND AN ELECTROMAGNETIC PULSE ERUPTS OUTWARD FROM HIS CHEST, DAMPING ALL ELECTRICAL SYSTEMS WITHIN A FIFTY-YARD RADIUS.
TELEVISION CAMERAS STOP ROLLING. LIGHTS GO OUT. TAPE RECORDERS SHUT DOWN.
AND G.W. BRIDGE'S S.H.I.E.L.D. AGENTS --
OUR JETPACKS! OUR GUNS!
BLAST!
ZEMO WAS PREPARED FOR US!
THIS -- THIS CAN'T BE HAPPENING! IT'S NOT TRUE, IT --
ATLAS -- GRAB MACH-1! HIS SYSTEMS HAVE SHUT DOWN TOO -- JUST AS TECHNO'S HAVE! THEY'LL REBOOT IN SIX MINUTES --
-- BUT IN THE MEANTIME, WE'LL HAVE TO CARRY THEM. SONGBIRD, YOU'RE SELF-POWERED -- WE NEED A BARRIER! AND METEORITE --

-- WE NEED AN *EXIT!*
ANY *PREFERENCES?*
THERE'S AN ***ACCESS CORRIDOR,*** UNDER THE STAGE -- IT LEADS TO THE ***BASEMENT!***
FOR SOMEONE WHO JUST GOT ZEMO -- YOU'RE AWFULLY *PREPARED!*
I AM ***ALWAYS*** PREPARED, METEORITE*!* NOW, THUNDERBOLTS --
--LET'S BE OFF!
AND AS THE THUNDERBOLTS VANISH THROUGH THE HASTILY-BLASTED OPENING...
DALLAS! I-- I --
BUT THERE'S NOTHING HE CAN SAY, HE REALIZES.
NOTHING AT ALL.
IT -- IT'S ***TRUE*** --
WE'D BETTER SPLIT UP. I CAN CARRY TECHNO, NOW THAT HIS SYSTEMS ARE DORMANT AND HE'S DIMINISHED IN SIZE. THE REST OF YOU --
-- WE'LL REGROUP AT ***HEADQUARTERS.*** DON'T GET SPOTTED -- BUT DON'T ***DELAY,*** EITHER.
HEY, WHERE'S JOLT?

LET JOLT WORRY ABOUT HERSELF, ATLAS! NOW GO!
CALL THE FANTASTIC FOUR! CALL THE HEROES FOR HIRE, THE NEW WARRIORS -- HECK, CALL THE X-MEN! BUT SOMEONE, ANYONE --
-- GET THE THUNDERBOLTS! STARTING WITH HER!
ALL SHE WANTED WAS TO BE A HERO.
SHE'D IDOLIZED SUPER HEROES FOR MOST OF HER LIFE -- AND WHEN THE THUNDERBOLTS OFFERED TO LET HER JOIN, SHE JUMPED AT THE CHANCE.
ALL RIGHT, MISSY --
-- YOU'RE COMING WITH ME!
AND NOW SHE'S GOING TO JAIL. SHE TRUSTED THEM. SHE DID HER BEST. BUT THEY LIED TO HER. AND NOW --
-- NOW --
NO!
SORRY, COLONEL BRIDGE, BUT I'M NOT GOING ANY-WHERE -- WITH ANY-ONE!
NOT UNTIL I FIGURE A FEW THINGS OUT!
AND LIKE THAT --
-- SHE'S GONE.
Huh?

AND AS JOLT EXITS TO THE EAST --
-- TO THE SOUTH, METEORITE ENCOUNTERS --
POOM
POOM
Eh? WHO?
HAWKEYE!
GOT IT IN ONE, MOONSTONE -- OR WHATEVER YOU'RE CALLING YOURSELF THESE DAYS!
I HAD A LITTLE BUSINESS HERE AT CITY HALL -- REESTABLISHING MY LEGAL BONA FIDES, WITH A LITTLE HELP FROM THE MARIA STARK FOUNDATION --
-- WHEN I CAUGHT THE SHOW YOU AND ZEMO'S OTHER LITTLE STORM-TROOPERS PUT ON!
NOW -- THOSE BLAST ARROWS WERE WARNING SHOTS. ARE YOU GOING TO SURRENDER --
-- OR WILL I HAVE TO INSIST?
I DON'T SUPPOSE YOU'D BELIEVE WE WERE SINCERE -- THAT WE REALLY DID WANT TO ATONE FOR OUR --
-- NO, NO, I SUPPOSE YOU WOULDN'T.
KRAMM
HEY!

A FALL LIKE THIS WOULD BE ENOUGH TO KILL AN ORDINARY MAN. BUT ORDINARY MEN DON'T THRIVE FOR YEARS AS MAINSTAYS OF THE AVENGERS --
-- AND EVEN AS HAWKEYE FALLS, HE'S REACHING FOR A PARTICULAR ARROW, FINDING IT BY ITS PLACE IN HIS QUIVER AND THE CODING ON ITS NOCK --
-- FINDING, DRAWING, NOCKING AND FIRING IT IN ONE SMOOTH MOTION --
-- AND IN LESS TIME THAN IT TAKES TO TELL --
CHK
-- HE'S ALREADY RECOVERED, ALREADY SWINGING FOR THE NEAREST ROOFTOP -- AND SCANNING THE SKIES FOR HIS TARGET.
YO, MOON-STAIN!
COME OUT, COME OUT, WHEREVER YOU ARE! C'MON, LET'S PLAY GOOD GUYS/BAD GUYS -- AN' I CALL DIBS ON THE WHITE HAT!
BUT METEORITE, A.K.A. MOON-STONE, A.K.A. Dr. KARLA SOFEN, ISN'T ALL THAT ORDINARY HERSELF -- AND SHE'S HAD EXPERIENCE WITH AVENGERS.
SO WHILE HAWKEYE'S SCANNING THE SKIES, SHE'S GOING TO GROUND. AND WITH A MOMENT'S THOUGHT --
-- SHE'S JUST ANOTHER PASSERBY.
SORRY, HAWKEYE -- BUT I DON'T FIGHT WITHOUT A REASON.
AND THERE MAY BE NO POINT LEFT EVEN TO REGROUP AT THE PLAZA -- THIS WAS A SWEET SET-UP WHILE IT LASTED, BUT IT'S BLOWN NOW.
MAYBE IT'S TIME TO CUT AND RUN, WHILE I STILL CAN. LET THE OTHERS FACE THE MUSIC --
-- WHILE I START OVER, SOMEWHERE ELSE...

MEANWHILE, IN A NARROW ALLEY TO THE WEST OF CITY HALL --
-- AN ALLEY WHOSE SHADOWED DEPTHS HAVE COME TO SEEM A REFUGE AGAINST THE CITY NOISES BEYOND ITS MOUTH...
FRA
ABE! ABE, ARE YOU ALL RIGHT?
Y-YEAH -- YEAH, BABE, I'M OKAY. MY SYSTEMS ARE COMING BACK ON LINE JUST FINE.
I SURE COULD'VE DONE WITH SOME WARNING, THOUGH...
LISTEN TO THEM OUT THERE. JUST AN HOUR AGO, THEY WERE CHEERING FOR US -- THEY LOVED US! AND NOW --
NOW WE'RE BACK IN THE COLD.
NICE, Huh?
LOOK! THERE'S TWO OF 'EM -- TWO OF THOSE LYING CREEPS!
LET'S GET 'EM!
WH-WHAT?
AND IN A MOMENT, THEIR ILLUSION OF REFUGE IS SHATTERED --
-- AND THEY'RE FLEEING AGAIN, STAYING LOW, STAYING IN THE ALLEYS, IN THE SHADOWS --
WE SHOULD HAVE LISTENED TO THE BLACK WIDOW. IF WE'D TURNED AGAINST ZEMO, LIKE SHE SUGGESTED --
THERE WASN'T TIME! SHE TOLD US SHE DIDN'T HAVE ANY EVIDENCE -- NOT YET!
I THOUGHT WE'D HAVE A CHANCE TO THINK -- TO MAKE A CHOICE!
-- BUT THOUGH THEIR BODIES ROCKET FORWARD, THEIR MINDS LOOK BACK -- BACK TO WHAT THEY'VE LOST...

AND TO THE NORTH...
SHE SNAGGED THE RAINCOAT THROUGH AN OPEN WINDOW, OFF THE BACK OF A CHAIR. MAKING HER A THIEF, ON TOP OF EVERYTHING ELSE.
SHE SHOULD HAVE KNOWN, SHE TELLS HERSELF.
BARON ZEMO, MOONSTONE, GOLIATH, THE FIXER, THE BEETLE -- AND SONGBIRD MUST BE SCREAMING MIMI. SHE SHOULD HAVE KNOWN.
THEY EVEN TOLD HER THEIR FIRST NAMES!
-- SECURITY CLEARANCE IS REVOKED, OF COURSE -- AND ALL ACCESS CODES TO SECURE SYSTEMS ARE BEING CHANGED IMMEDIATELY.
WE WILL NOT REST UNTIL THESE HEINOUS CRIMINALS ARE CAPTURED AND IMPRISONED. AND MORE THAN THAT --
-- I WILL BE FERRETING OUT THOSE ON MY STAFF WHO LED ME ASTRAY -- LED ME TO TRUST THESE MONSTERS!
IN ADDITION TO THIS MORNING'S BOMBSHELL --
-- INDEPENDENT CONFIRMATION IS COMING IN, AS IN THIS FOOTAGE FROM THE THUNDERBOLTS' BATTLE WITH ARNIM ZOLA --
SONGBIRD, MOONSTONE -- LISTEN! HE'S USING ENORMOUS POWER TO ANIMATE STONE --
H-Huh?
SHE WAS THERE. SHE SHOULD HAVE NOTICED THAT. BUT -- BUT THEY WERE SO NICE, SO HEROIC --
THE MASTERS OF EVIL ARE PERHAPS BEST KNOWN FOR THEIR VIRTUAL DESTRUCTION OF AVENGERS MANSION, BACK IN --
SHE KNEW THEM. SHE LIVED WITH THEM, FOUGHT WITH THEM.
IT CAN'T BE TRUE. NOT -- NOT ALL OF IT.
IT CAN'T BE.

AND, AT FOUR FREEDOMS PLAZA...
OKAY, FOLKS -- THE NEW WARRIORS ARE HERE! WHAT'S THE SITCH?
MACH-1 AND SONGBIRD MADE IT IN JUST AS SPIDEY AND I GOT HERE -- WE DON'T KNOW IF ANYONE ELSE GOT HERE BEFORE THEM.
THE HEROES FOR HIRE ARE OFF ON A CASE, AND THE FANTASTIC FOUR APPARENTLY CAN'T BE REACHED. AS FOR THE PLAZA ITSELF --
-- THE BUILDING'S AUTOMATED DEFENSES ARE KEEPING EVERY-BODY WELL AWAY FROM IT!
YOW!
KOOM
I SEE WHAT YOU MEAN!
ATLAS WATCHES FROM CONCEALMENT, FRUSTRATED AND NERVOUS. HE'D STUCK TO ROOFTOPS GETTING HERE, TO AVOID DETECTION --
-- FOR ALL THE GOOD IT DID. THE BUILDING'S DEFENSES WOULD LET HIM THROUGH. ONCE HE WAS INSIDE, HE'D BE JUST FINE --
-- IF HE COULD GET PAST ALL THE SUPER HEROES, THAT IS --!

WHOOAAAAAAA
SHUT UP, ATLAS. AND TRY TO BE SLEEKER, WILL YOU -- YOU'RE SLOWING ME DOWN!
METEORITE --?! I'D HAVE FIGURED YOU TO BE HALFWAY TO BRAZIL BY NOW!
Huh?
YEAH, ME TOO. BUT I DECIDED I'M TOO INVESTED IN THIS TO JUST WALK AWAY -- AND THERE STILL MIGHT BE A CHANCE TO SALVAGE SOMETHING.
HEY!
WE CAN MAKE IT INTO THE DEFENSE PRIMETER BEFORE THESE FOOLS CAN REACT -- AND THEN, WELL, THEN WE'LL SEE WHAT HAPPENS!
WHA --?
AT THAT MOMENT, BELOW THE STREET...
...JOLT SHORTS OUT THE MAGNETIC LOCK ON THE SEWER ENTRANCE TO THE PLAZA SUB-BASEMENTS.
WARNING
IVATE ACCES
SHE'S HAD SOME TIME TO THINK, NOW, TO WORK THINGS OUT.
THEY HAVEN'T CHANGED THE CODES. THAT GETS HER INTO THE ELEVATOR SHAFT.
SHE'S NOT JUST GOING TO GET ARRESTED, GO TO JAIL, AND LEAVE IT AT THAT.

THERE'S GOT TO BE SOMETHING SHE CAN DO. SOMETHING SHE CAN FIND OUT, SOME WAY SHE CAN FIX THIS.
MAYBE SHE'S KIDDING HERSELF -- MAYBE ALL SHE CAN DO IS GET HERSELF KILLED --
-- BUT UNDER THE CIRCUMSTANCES, IT'S WORTH A TRY. AND IT SURE BEATS THE HECK OUT OF GIVING UP.
CITY ENGINEERS ARE WORKING ON THE EXTERIOR ACCESS TO THE BUILDING'S SYSTEMS ALREADY. THEY'RE NOT HAVING MUCH LUCK --
-- BUT THEY'LL GET THERE. WE'VE GOT LESS THAN FIFTEEN MINUTES BEFORE THEY GAIN CONTROL OF OUR DEFENSES, AND SHUT US DOWN.
Oh, FABULOUS.
WHAT I WANT TO KNOW IS, WHO EXPOSED US? WHO FIGURED IT OUT?
I'D LIKE TO KNOW THAT, TOO. DALLAS AN' I, WE -- WELL, I JUST KEEP REMEMBERIN' THE LOOK ON HER FACE --
-- AN' I'D SURE LIKE TO GET MY HANDS ON WHOEVER MESSED UP THINGS FOR US -- FOR ALL OF US!
IT WAS THE BLACK WIDOW. IT HAS TO HAVE BEEN -- SHE ALL BUT PROMISED TO DO IT A FEW DAYS AGO!
THE BLACK WIDOW? MACH-1, WHAT ARE YOU TALKING AB--
RELAX, METEORITE. THE BLACK WIDOW IS THE LEAST OF YOUR CONCERNS, AT THE MOMENT.
IN ANY CASE, IT WASN'T SHE WHO ENDED OUR LITTLE PERFORMANCE --

-- IT WAS I!
AND I MUST SAY, IT FEELS GOOD TO CAST OFF THAT ANNOYINGLY-IDEALISTIC FACADE -- AND RETURN TO MY TRUE SELF!
ZEMO? BUT -- BUT WHY --
BECAUSE I KNEW, BEETLE. I AM ZEMO -- DID YOU THINK ANY OF WHAT HAS BEEN GOING ON IN YOUR TINY MINDS HAS ESCAPED MY NOTICE?
I AM ZEMO. I MISS NOTHING.
YOU WERE THINKING OF ABANDONING THE PLAN -- OF PLAYING THE ROLE OF HEROES FOREVER, SINCE YOU'VE ENJOYED IT SO MUCH.
AND MOONSTONE WAS NUDGING YOU ALL ALONG TOWARD THAT DECISION, TO SATISFY HER OWN AMBITIONS. DID YOU TRULY THINK I DIDN'T KNOW?
I LET IT HAPPEN -- I LET YOU PLAY YOUR GAMES!
AFTER ALL, IT KEPT YOU OCCUPIED -- AND I KNEW IT WOULD GO NOWHERE. YOU WOULD DITHER AND FRET AND HOPE AND PLAN --
-- AND I, WHEN THE TIME WAS RIGHT, WOULD CLOSE THAT DOOR BEFORE YOU COULD GO THROUGH IT -- AS, INDEED, I HAVE.

YOU COULD HAVE WARNED US!
WE COULD HAVE BEEN CAPTURED -- ANY OF US! WE COULD HAVE BEEN KILLED!
YES, GOLIATH -- YOU COULD HAVE BEEN. I DEEMED IT A NECESSARY STEP -- A WAY OF CLEARLY DEMONSTRATING YOUR SITUATION.
AFTER ALL, YOU KNOW WHERE YOU STAND NOW -- YOU KNOW YOUR OPTIONS. YOU CAN RETURN TO YOUR ADORING PUBLIC, IF YOU LIKE --
-- AND BE TORN LIMB FROM LIMB.
YOU CAN BECOME INDEPENDENT SUPER-VILLAINS ONCE MORE -- AND SEE WHAT KIND OF RECEPTION THE UNDERWORLD WILL GIVE YOU --
-- NOW THAT THEY KNOW WHAT YOU'VE DONE TO THEM.
OR YOU CAN STAY WITH ME.
IT'S ENTIRELY UP TO YOU.
ENTIRELY UP TO THEM. YEAH, RIGHT.
SOME CHOICE.

HAH!
MY FATHER WAS RIGHT -- CONTROL HOPE, AND YOU CONTROL ALL. BUT HE NEVER TOOK IT THIS FAR -- NEVER!
ENOUGH SELF-CONGRATULATION, THOUGH. WE HAVE WORK TO DO.
COME ALONG, MY NEWLY-FAITHFUL FOLLOWERS. THE CITY ENGINEERS ARE DOUBTLESS ABOUT TO SHUT DOWN OUR EMERGENCY-GENERATORS --
"-- SO IT BEHOOVES US TO TAKE OUR LEAVE."
WHERE -- WHERE ARE WE GOING?
YOU'LL SEE SOON ENOUGH, SCREAMING MIMI. BUT AT THE MOMENT --
HEY -- THEY'RE MAKIN' A BREAK FOR IT!
-- IT'S TIME TO DISCOURAGE PURSUIT. AND THE BEST WAY TO DO THAT --
-- IS WITH A LITTLE PARTING GIFT THE FIXER AND I HAVE PREPARED FOR THE GOOD PEOPLE AND HEROES OF NEW YORK CITY...
TEK

KA-WOOOM!
FOUR FREEDOMS PLAZA HAS NOT GRACED THE MANHATTAN SKYLINE FOR LONG, BUT IT HAS NONETHELESS COME TO OCCUPY A SPECIAL PLACE IN THE HEARTS OF NEW YORKERS.
BUILT TO SERVE AS THE FANTASTIC FOUR'S HEADQUARTERS AFTER THE DESTRUCTION OF THE BAXTER BUILDING, THE SIGHT OF IT LOOMING OVER MID-MANHATTAN HAS BEEN A SIGN OF SECURITY FOR MILLIONS.
NO LONGER.
THE TOP STORIES ARE GONE IN AN INSTANT -- AND THEN A SERIES OF LESSER EXPLOSIONS RIPS DOWN THE LENGTH OF THE SKYSCRAPER --
-- SHATTERING THE BUILDING'S SKELETON, COLLAPSING THE OFFICES THAT FILL MOST OF THE STRUCTURE LIKE SO MUCH CARDBOARD.
THE BUILDING HAD BEEN EVACUATED, ONCE AUTHORITIES CORDONED IT OFF, BUT EVEN THAT MEASURE ONLY MITIGATES THE DANGER --

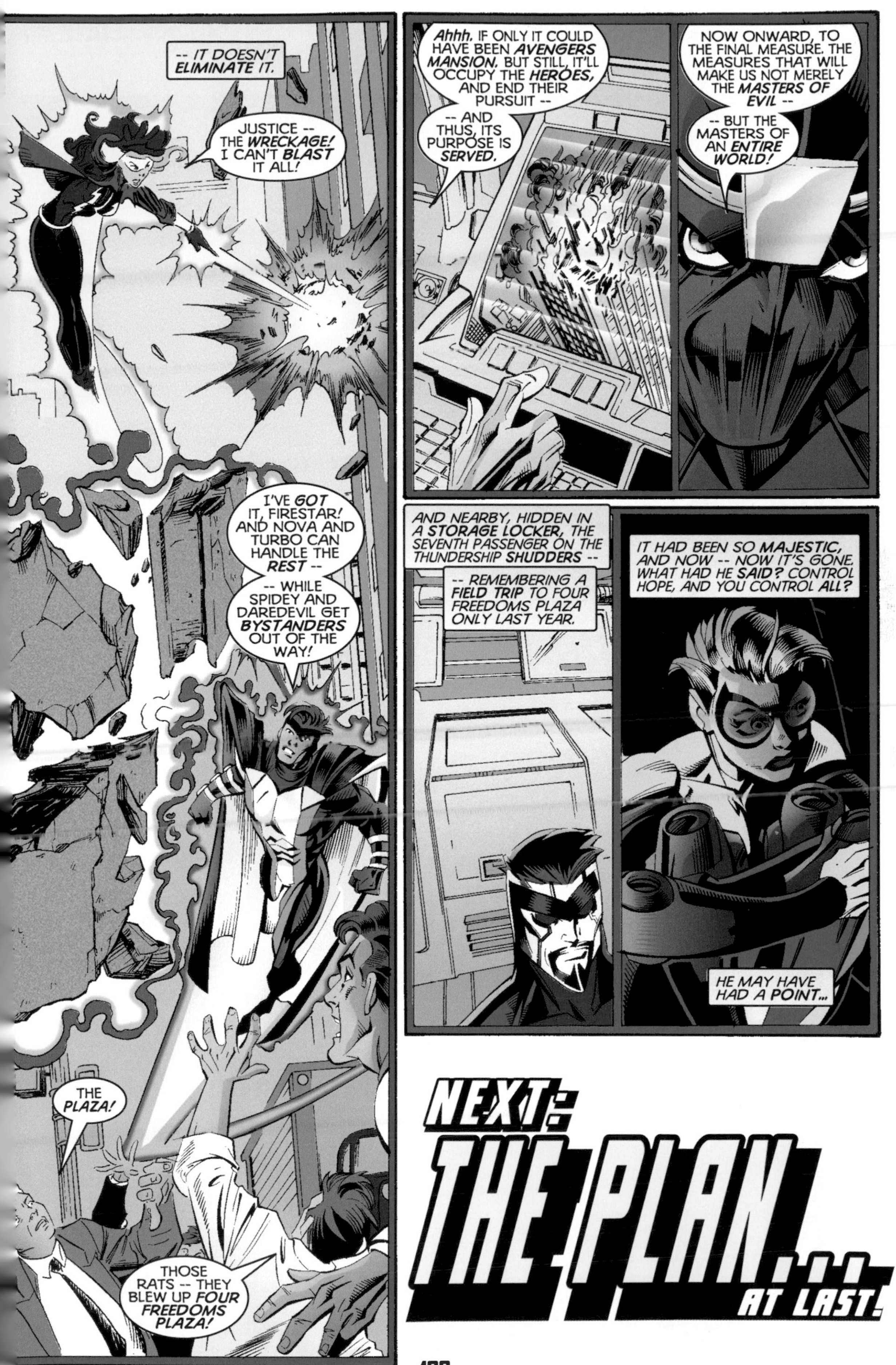
-- IT DOESN'T ELIMINATE IT.
JUSTICE -- THE WRECKAGE! I CAN'T BLAST IT ALL!
I'VE GOT IT, FIRESTAR! AND NOVA AND TURBO CAN HANDLE THE REST --
-- WHILE SPIDEY AND DAREDEVIL GET BYSTANDERS OUT OF THE WAY!
THE PLAZA!
THOSE RATS -- THEY BLEW UP FOUR FREEDOMS PLAZA!
Ahhh. IF ONLY IT COULD HAVE BEEN AVENGERS MANSION. BUT STILL, IT'LL OCCUPY THE HEROES, AND END THEIR PURSUIT --
-- AND THUS, ITS PURPOSE IS SERVED.
NOW ONWARD, TO THE FINAL MEASURE. THE MEASURES THAT WILL MAKE US NOT MERELY THE MASTERS OF EVIL --
-- BUT THE MASTERS OF AN ENTIRE WORLD!
AND NEARBY, HIDDEN IN A STORAGE LOCKER, THE SEVENTH PASSENGER ON THE THUNDERSHIP SHUDDERS --
-- REMEMBERING A FIELD TRIP TO FOUR FREEDOMS PLAZA ONLY LAST YEAR.
IT HAD BEEN SO MAJESTIC, AND NOW -- NOW IT'S GONE. WHAT HAD HE SAID? CONTROL HOPE, AND YOU CONTROL ALL?
HE MAY HAVE HAD A POINT...
NEXT:
THE PLAN...
AT LAST.

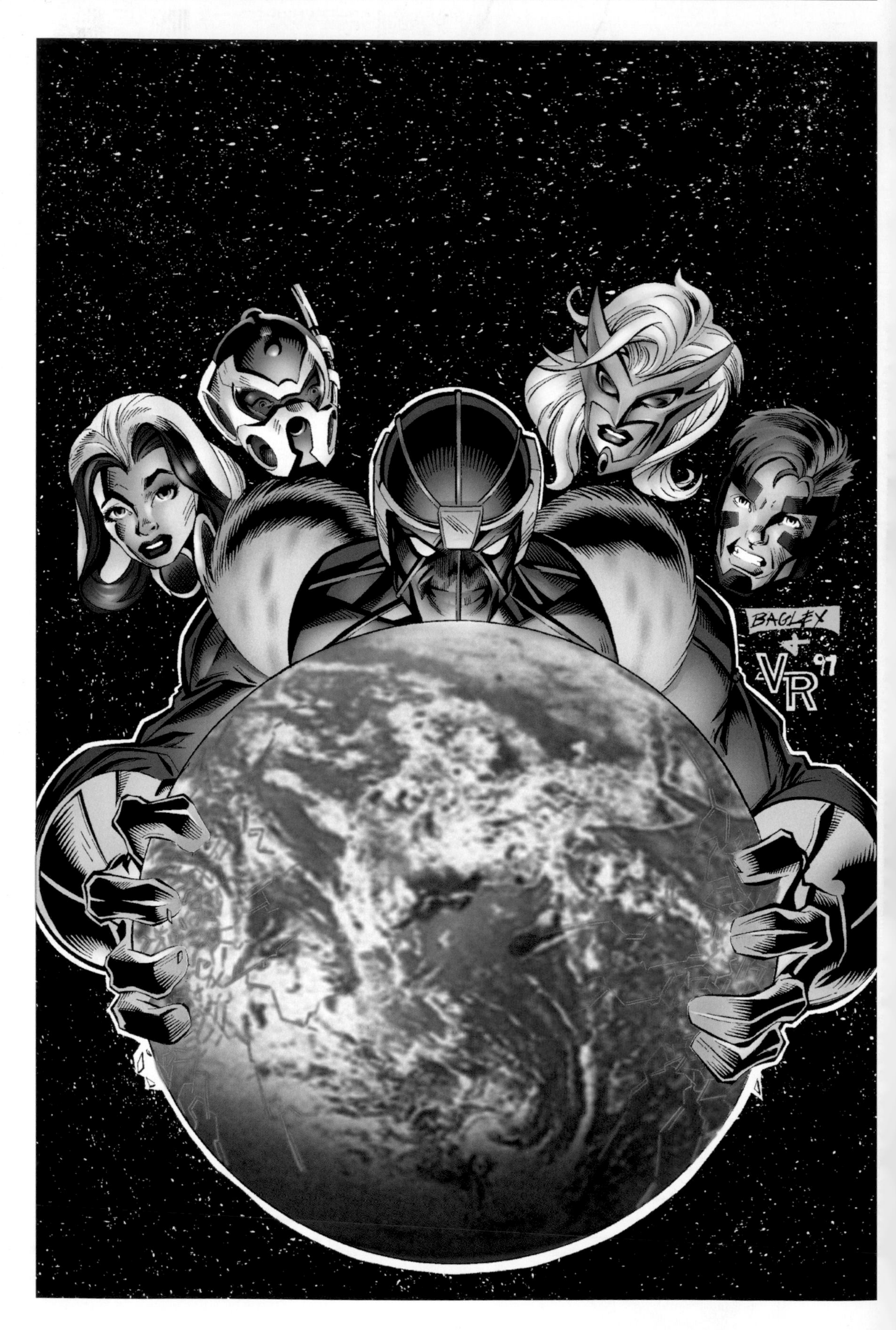
BAGLEY
+
VR 97

LIBERTAD, CAPITOL OF THE TINY CENTRAL AMERICAN NATION OF SANTO RICO.
THIS CITY SQUARE HAS KNOWN PEACE FOR YEARS -- SINCE GIANT-MAN AND THE WASP DEPOSED THE BRUTAL EL TORO --
-- SO IT'S ALL THE MORE SHOCKING FOR THE SANTO RICANS TO SEE IT ONCE MORE FILLED WITH TANKS AND ARMED MEN --
-- AS A MILITARY JUNTA FORCES THEIR PRESIDENT TO SURRENDER THE COUNTRY TO ITS CONTROL.
THE COUP CAME SWIFTLY, RUTH-LESSLY, AND WITH-OUT WARNING -- AND ITS MADNESS IS NOT CONFINED TO SANTO RICO.
ALL AROUND THE WORLD, THE SCENARIO REPEATS ITSELF --
-- FROM CAIRO --
BRATTA
‹SWIFTLY, MY COMPATRIOTS! SECURE THE TOWN!›
-- TO OSLO --
‹THERE IS NO REASON TO BE CONCERNED, CITIZENS! WE HAVE TAKEN COMMAND OF THE NATION, BUT NO ONE WILL BE HARMED IF THEY OBEY!›
‹ORDER WILL BE SWIFTLY RESTORED!›
-- TO BOOTH CITY, NEVADA --
THIS IS INSANE! THIS IS THE UNITED STATES -- YOU'RE AMERICAN SOLDIERS!
YOU CAN'T DO THIS!
SILENCE! YOU WILL ACCEDE TO OUR DEMANDS IMMEDIATELY -- OR YOU WILL BE SHOT!
BOOTH CITY HALL

A-AND WHAT ARE YOUR DEMANDS?
NOTHING LESS THAN TOTAL SURRENDER -- SURRENDER TO THE RULE OF ZEMO!
AVENGERS MANSION, ON FIFTH AVENUE IN MANHATTAN.
ANY WORD, REED?
NOTHING YET, CAPTAIN AMERICA. APPARENTLY, ZEMO'S TAKEN CONTROL OF CONSIDERABLE NUMBERS OF MILITARY PERSONNEL AROUND THE WORLD --
-- BUT WE HAVE NO IDEA HOW HE DID IT, OR EVEN WHERE HE IS.
HE CAN'T HAVE SIMPLY DISAPPEARED--!
BELIEVE ME, CAP -- IF WE KNEW WHERE THE CREEP WUZ, WE'D BE ALL OVER 'IM, AN' YOU'D BE INVITED TA THE PARTY!
BUT HIM AN' HIS CREEP TEAM-MATES, BLEW UP OUR BUILDING -- BLEW UP FOUR FREEDOMS PLAZA --
-- AN' NOBODY'S SEEN HIDE NOR HAIR OF 'EM IN THE WEEKS SINCE!
VERILY, IT DOTH DEFY UNDERSTANDING!
YOU SAID IT, THOR. WHY, THERE ARE TROOPS -- AMERICANS -- MARCHING ON NEW YORK CITY EVEN AS WE SPEAK!
GOOD THING NOT EVERY-ONE'S AFFECTED -- THE NATIONAL GUARD'S FORTIFYING THE CITY EVEN NOW. BUT IF WE CAN'T STOP THIS --
WE'LL STOP IT, IRON MAN. WE'LL STOP IT.
I KNOW YOU'LL MAKE EVERY EFFORT, REED -- AND THAT YOU, BEN AND THE REST OF THE FANTASTIC FOUR STAND READY TO ACT.
WE AVENGERS DON'T HAVE A SETTLED ROSTER YET, BUT WE'VE GOT AN AD HOC TEAM ASSEMBLED AND READY TO GO --

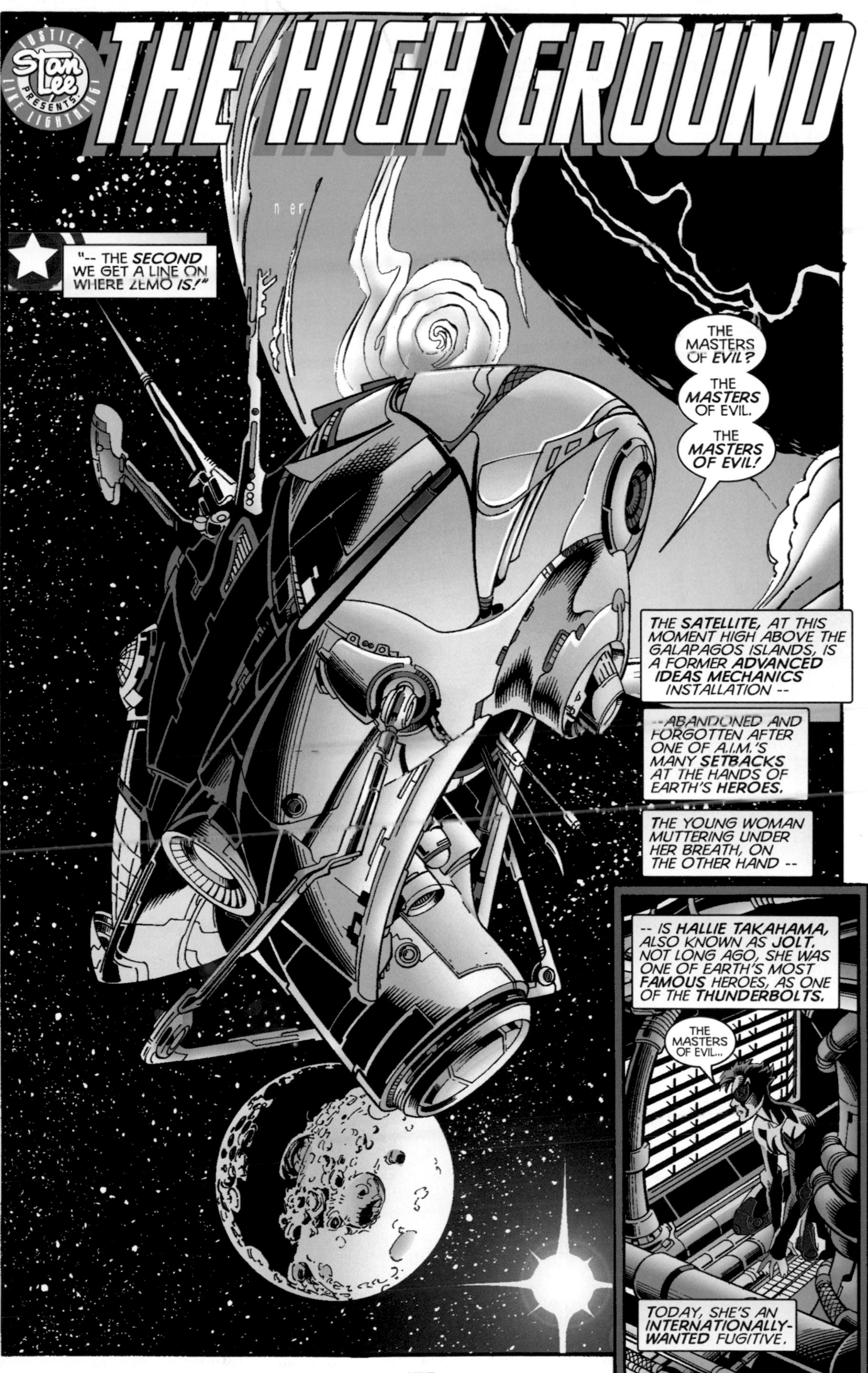
STAN LEE PRESENTS
JUSTICE LIKE LIGHTNING!
THE HIGH GROUND
"-- THE SECOND WE GET A LINE ON WHERE ZEMO IS!"
THE MASTERS OF EVIL?
THE MASTERS OF EVIL.
THE MASTERS OF EVIL!
THE SATELLITE, AT THIS MOMENT HIGH ABOVE THE GALAPAGOS ISLANDS, IS A FORMER ADVANCED IDEAS MECHANICS INSTALLATION --
--ABANDONED AND FORGOTTEN AFTER ONE OF A.I.M.'S MANY SETBACKS AT THE HANDS OF EARTH'S HEROES.
THE YOUNG WOMAN MUTTERING UNDER HER BREATH, ON THE OTHER HAND --
-- IS HALLIE TAKAHAMA, ALSO KNOWN AS JOLT. NOT LONG AGO, SHE WAS ONE OF EARTH'S MOST FAMOUS HEROES, AS ONE OF THE THUNDERBOLTS.
THE MASTERS OF EVIL...
TODAY, SHE'S AN INTERNATIONALLY-WANTED FUGITIVE.

WHEN SHE JOINED THE TEAM, SHE DIDN'T KNOW THEY WERE SECRETLY THE ELITE CADRE SUPER-VILLAINS KNOWN AS THE MASTERS OF EVIL -- POSING AS HEROES TO WORM THEIR WAY PAST THE WORLD'S DEFENSES.
BUT THAT WAS BEFORE THEY DROPPED THE CHARADE -- BEFORE SHE STOWED AWAY ON THEIR ESCAPE CRAFT --
-- AND NOW SHE WATCHES THEM -- SONGBIRD, MACH-1, METEORITE -- ONCE HER CLOSEST FRIENDS --
WHAT'S WRONG, ABE? YOU'RE PACING LIKE A CAT!
I DON'T LIKE THIS, BABE. I DON'T LIKE THE WAITING, I DON'T LIKE THE-- I JUST DON'T LIKE IT, THAT'S ALL! WE WERE FINE THE WAY WE WERE!
YOU DON'T LIKE WHAT, BEETLE? DON'T LIKE THE FACT THAT IF ZEMO SUCCEEDS, YOU'LL BE ONE OF THE MASTERS OF THE WORLD?
-- AND KNOWS THEM FOR WHO THEY REALLY ARE: SCREAMING MIMI, THE BEETLE AND MOONSTONE. IT'S TRUE, SHE REMINDS HERSELF. IT'S TRUE.
LOOK, DON'T CALL ME THAT, OKAY? AND YEAH, MAYBE I'LL BE IN CHARGE, AND PEOPLE WILL FEAR ME, AND BOW TO ME, AND ALL.
BUT, WELL, I GUESS I LIKED IT BETTER -- WHEN THEY JUST LIKED ME.
THERE'S AN EDGE TO MOONSTONE'S HONEYED VOICE, AND JOLT WONDERS -- IS SHE REASSURING MACH-1, OR MAKING HIM REALIZE HIS MISTAKE?
TIME ENOUGH TO THINK ABOUT THAT LATER, THOUGH. RIGHT NOW...
...SHE'D BETTER CHECK ON ZEMO.
INCOMING DATA, BARON -- AND SINCE I'M MERGED WITH THE STATION COMPUTERS, I'M RECEIVING IT CYBERNETICALLY. CONVENIENT, Eh?
YOUR CROWING OVER YOUR NEW ROBOTIC BODY IS RAPIDLY GROWING TIRESOME, FIXER. WHAT'S THE NEWS?
ANOTHER FOUR NATIONS FALLEN -- MAKING A TOTAL OF THIRTY-SIX, SO FAR.

EXCELLENT, FIXER -- EXCELLENT!
AND HAD WE STUCK TO OUR ORIGINAL PLAN -- TO PLANT A CONTROL VIRUS IN THE WORLD'S MILITARY COMPUTER SYSTEMS ONCE WE GAINED ACCESS AS THE THUNDERBOLTS -- WE'D BE NOWHERE NEAR THIS FAR ALONG!
BUT INSTEAD, WE PLANTED A RECOGNITION CODE -- ALLOWING US ACCESS EVEN AFTER THEY SUPPOSEDLY SHUT US OUT --
-- AND THANKS TO OUR FORESIGHT IN DUPLICATING THE PLANS FOR THE BIO-MODEM, WE'RE ABLE TO DO FAR, FAR MORE!
Ah, THAT'D BE MY FORESIGHT, BARON. I'M THE ONE WHO COPIED THE DATA ON THE BIO-MODEM.
YES, YES, HOWEVER IT HAPPENED. THE IMPORTANT THING IS, WE DID IT.
Ah, TO HAVE SEEN THEIR FACES --
"-- NOT KNOWING THE BIO-MODEM SIGNAL WAS BEING PIPED INTO THEIR SYSTEMS -- RECONFIGURING THEIR PROGRAMMING, THEIR HARDWARE --
"-- ALTERING THE ELECTRON GUNS IN THEIR MONITORS --
"-- AND TAKING THEIR MINDS IN AN INSTANT'S EXPOSURE!
"AND THE FIRST TO BE TAKEN BECAME OUR SPIES, OUR SABOTEURS --"
SIRS? IT'S THE COMPUTERS, SIR --
-- I THINK YOU BETTER SEE THIS FOR YOURSELVES.
"-- AND THE REST FELL LIKE DOMINOES. JUST LIKE DOMINOES."
HAPPY TO BE OF SERVICE, BARON.
BUT SAY -- WOULD YOU LIKE TO SPEAK TO YOUR SUBJECTS? I'VE BEEN MONITORING TELECOMMUNICATIONS, BUT I COULD BREAK IN...
I -- YES, FIXER. I THINK I'D LIKE THAT. SEE TO IT, IF YOU WOULD.

NO PROBLEM, BARON. BUT MAKE IT "TECHNO," OKAY? THE NAME JUST SEEMS TO GO WITH THE NEW BODY, AFTER ALL --
-- AND WHEN THE BODY CAN FORM A STATE-OF-THE-ART-VIDEO CAMERA, SIMPLY BECAUSE I ABSORBED THE SCHEMATICS TO --
YES, YES, TECHNO. VERY IMPRESSIVE. JUST GET ON WITH IT, WOULD YOU?
TECHNO SMILES, AND INCLINES HIS HEAD IN AN ACCOMMODATING NOD. AND THE MOMENT HE DOES, ALL AROUND THE PLANET --
PEOPLE OF EARTH, GREETINGS. I AM HELMUT, THIRTEENTH BARON ZEMO -- OR, MORE ACCURATELY, I AM ZEMO, FIRST EMPEROR OF THE WORLD!
MY TROOPS ARE ADVANCING THROUGH VIRTUALLY EVERY PART OF THE GLOBE, AND THEY CANNOT -- THEY WILL NOT -- BE CHECKED.
MOM, WHAT --
BILLY, SHH!
TELL THEM TO CAPITULATE -- THAT IF THEY SURRENDER NOW, I WILL BE MERCIFUL, AND PEACE CAN REIGN ONCE MORE. BUT IF YOU RESIST --
-- I WILL CRUSH YOU INTO THE DIRT, AND BUILD MY EMPIRE ON THE RUBBLE. THE CHOICE IS YOURS. THAT IS ALL.
<YOUR LEADERS WILL TALK OF RESISTANCE, OF STANDING FIRM. BUT THEY KNOW, AS YOU DO, THAT THEY ARE MERELY DELAYING THE INEVITABLE --
<-- AND THAT THEY ARE BUYING TIME AT THE COST OF YOUR LIVES.>
QUE?
IN RESPONSE, THE NATIONAL GUARDSMEN IN TIMES SQUARE CLENCH THEIR JAWS HARDER AND AWAIT THE COMING BATTLE --
-- BUT THAT IS NOT THE ONLY REACTION. IN THE BALKAN NATION OF CARNELIA, NESTLED IN AMONG THE CARPATHIAN ALPS...
<WE MUST STRIKE BACK WHILE WE ARE STILL FREE! FIRE OUR MISSILES AT THE SOURCE OF THIS MADMAN'S BROADCAST SIGNAL!>

<BUT, MY PREMIER -- WE CANNOT LOCK ON TO THE SIGNAL! IT COMES FROM ORBIT, BUT--
<-- BUT IT KEEPS SHIFTING -- DEFYING OUR ABILITY TO TRACK IT!>
<I DO NOT CARE, GENERAL! GUESS, IF YOU HAVE TO! GUESS --
<-- BUT FIRE THOSE MISSILES!>
SLOWLY, MAJESTICALLY, THE MISSILES RISE ON THEIR LAUNCHERS, THEIR NOSES STRAINING TOWARD THE SKY--
-- ALL AIMED TOWARD ONE TINY SPOT IN THE HEAVENS.
AND THEN, THE LAUNCH BUTTON IS PRESSED --
KRROOM
WHOM
WHOM
-- AND THE CARNELIAN COUNTRYSIDE IS ROCKED BY THEIR FURY, AS THEY VIOLENTLY EXPLODE WHERE THEY STAND.
TSK-TSK. AS IF, SIMPLY BECAUSE WE DID NOT HAVE ALL OF THEIR MILITARY YET -- WE DID NOT HAVE THEIR MISSILES, AS WELL.
EASTERN EUROPE IS FORTUNATE THAT CARNELIA DID NOT HAVE NUCLEAR CAPACITY--
-- BUT NEVERTHELESS, THIS EPISODE SHOULD SERVE TO DEMONSTRATE OUR COMPLETE AND UTTER CONTROL TO THE REST OF THE WORLD.
HIS VOICE IS COLD AND BRISK AND HARD, BUT THERE'S SOMETHING IN IT --
-- SOMETHING SHE CAN'T QUITE IDENTIFY --

EVERYONE'LL THINK TWICE ABOUT LAUNCHING ANOTHER ATTACK -- EVEN IF THEY COULD FIND US.
BUT HEY, HOW'D YOU LIKE THE INSTANT TRANSLATION I DID WITH THE AUDIO TRANSMISSION? EVERY COUNTRY HEARD YOU IN THEIR OWN LANGUAGE.
ALL PART OF THE --
YES, BUT WHERE IS THE SATISFACTION IN RULING A PLANET OF AUTOMATONS, Hmm? BETTER TO BREAK THEIR SPIRITS THAN ENSLAVE THEIR MINDS.
BETTER IF THEY KNOW THEY HAVE BEEN CONQUERED.
AND THEN IT HITS HER. HE'S ENJOYING THIS. HE'S ENJOYING THIS.
Uh-Oh! WE'VE GOT A SECURITY BREACH -- A COMM-SIGNAL.
COMING IN?
NO. GOING OUT.
YES, YES. YOUR NEW BODY IS MOST VERSATILE, TECHNO -- THERE IS NO END TO ITS CAPACITIES. IS THAT WHAT YOU WISH TO HEAR?
IT'LL DO. BUT I'VE GOT A QUESTION: WHY NOT JUST CONTROL EVERY-ONE WITH THE BIO-MODEM? WE COULD DO IT...
GRACIE MANSION, MANHATTAN.
Ms. RIORDAN -- HEY, DALLAS! YOU'VE GOT A CALL COMING IN ON YOUR COMPUTER! IT'S --
-- CRIPES!
IT'S ATLAS -- OF THE THUNDERBOLTS! HE'S SIGNALING FOR A VIDEO LINK!
YOU'RE KIDDING!
QUICK -- RUN A TRACE ON THE CALL! RUN A TRACE!

Uh -- HI, BABE. I, Uh, LOOK, I JUST WANTED TO SAY --
I NEVER MEANT TO -- I DIDN'T WANT TO --
YOU DIDN'T WANT TO WHAT?! YOU NEVER MEANT TO WHAT?!
BLAST YOU, YOU ACTED LIKE MY FRIEND -- LIKE YOU LOVED ME! AND ALL THE TIME -- YOU WERE LYING TO ME!
YOU USED ME, YOU BETRAYED ME -- YOU'RE TAKING OVER THE WHOLE FREAKING WORLD BY FORCE --
-- AND YOU THINK YOU CAN APOLOGIZE FOR THAT?!
I -- NO, NO, I CAN'T. BUT I -- I WANTED YOU TO KNOW HOW I --
THAT'S IT! KEEP HIM TALKING!
PKAKT
NO -- WE'VE BEEN CUT OFF! GOT TO GET HER BACK -- TELL HER I KNOW SHE HATES ME, BUT I WASN'T -- WASN'T LYING ABOUT --
JOSTEN.
WOULD YOU LIKE TO TELL ME WHY YOU'RE RISKING COMPROMISING OUR SECURITY -- WHY YOU'RE DISOBEYING MY DIRECT ORDERS?
Uh -- SORRY, BOSS. I JUST -- I JUST WANTED TO SEE HER FACE, THAT'S ALL.
WOMEN ARE A WEAKNESS, ERIK. A GOOD SOLDIER KNOWS THAT. YOU KNOW THAT. DON'T FORGET IT AGAIN, UNDERSTAND?
Uh, YESSIR.
WELL, THERE'S NO HARM DONE, IN ANY CASE. THE ENCRYPTION CLOAKING MODULE WORKED PERFECTLY. AS LONG AS WE'VE GOT IT --
-- NOBODY'LL BE ABLE TO TRACE US, WHATEVER SIGNALS WE SEND. I GUARANTEE IT.
SHE STARTS TO GET AN IDEA, THEN -- OR AT LEAST THE BEGINNINGS OF ONE.
BUT A LOT OF IT'LL DEPEND ON THE OTHERS...

AND, LATER...
LOOK AT IT DOWN THERE. THE EARTH. YOU FIGURE THOSE LIGHTS DOWN THERE -- THEY'RE BATTLES?
SOME OF 'EM, ANY-WAY. AND ACCORDING TO TECHNO, WE'RE WINNING 'EM. FIFTY-THREE NATIONS HAVE SURRENDERED SO FAR.
IT'S FUNNY. WE'RE WINNING. WE'RE GOING TO BE RULERS OF THE ENTIRE PLANET. SO WHY --
-- WHY DO I HATE IT SO MUCH?
BECAUSE, ABE JENKINS, YOU'VE NEVER UNDERSTOOD WHAT YOU TRULY WANT OUT OF LIFE. NONE OF YOU HAVE.
YOU THINK YOU WANT POWER, ABE, BUT WHAT YOU REALLY WANT IS RESPECT. SONG-BIRD WANTS TO BELONG SOMEWHERE -- WITH SOMEONE.
AND ATLAS JUST WANTS TO BE TOLD WHAT TO DO, SO HE DOESN'T HAVE TO THINK FOR HIMSELF. ISN'T THAT RIGHT, ATLAS?
I WANT -- I WANT -- HEY!
DON'T WORRY, FOLKS. IT'S JUST ME -- THAT LITTLE KID YOU TOOK IN, THE ONE YOU TREATED LIKE A DAUGHTER. THE ONE YOU TOLD YOU WERE HEROES...
JOLT!
GEEZ, I FIGURED YOU WERE STILL IN NEW YORK -- BUT YOU WEREN'T ON THE NEWS OR NOTHING, LIKE THEY HADN'T FOUND YOU!
SO HOW'D YOU GET UP HERE, ANYWAY?
STOWED AWAY -- AND IT'S A GOOD THING I DID, OR I'D HAVE BEEN IN FOUR FREEDOMS PLAZA WHEN IT BLEW UP.
NO! AND YOU'VE BEEN HERE ALL THIS TIME?
SO WHY COME FORWARD NOW?
BECAUSE I THINK I KNOW HOW TO TAKE ZEMO DOWN --
-- BUT I'M GOING TO NEED YOUR HELP.

WH-WHAT --?
US? GO UP AGAINST ZEMO? YOU'RE CRAZY -- WE WOULDN'T STAND A CHANCE!
YES -- YES, WE WOULD! WE'RE INSIDE HIS DEFENSES -- HE WOULDN'T BE EXPECTING ANYTHING!
WE CAN PULL THIS OFF!
I KNOW YOU -- I KNOW YOU'RE NOT THE COLD-HEARTED KILLERS YOU'RE MADE OUT TO BE. I'VE LIVED WITH YOU -- FOUGHT ALONGSIDE YOU --
-- AND I KNOW YOU LIKED BEING HEROES. I KNOW IT FELT GOOD FOR YOU TO DO THE RIGHT THING, AND THAT YOU DON'T WANT THIS.
AM I WRONG? ABE? MELISSA? ERIK? CAN YOU HONESTLY TELL ME I'M WRONG?
WELL...
Ah...
YOU KNOW... THERE MIGHT JUST BE SOME POSSIBILITIES INHERENT IN THIS IDEA...
Oh?
POSSIBILITIES FOR WHAT, MOONSTONE? POSSIBILITIES TO FREE THE WORLD -- OR TO TAKE ZEMO DOWN AND RULE IN HIS PLACE?
Ah, CHILD. YOU BELIEVE IN THEM, BUT NOT ME. AND WHY SHOULD YOU? I LIED TO YOU THE MOST SERIOUSLY, AFTER ALL.
BUT I ASSURE YOU --
AND HOW CAN YOU ASSURE ANYONE OF ANYTHING, Dr. SOFEN --

-- YOU WHO HAVE NEVER SPOKEN A WORD IN YOUR LIFE THAT WAS NOT CALCULATED TO BRING YOU ADVANTAGE?
HOW CAN ANYONE EVER TRUST YOU?
ZEMO!
Oh, NO!
JOSTEN. RETURN TO YOUR MASTER.
A-ATLAS..?
LOOK AT YOU. THE BOLD MUTINEERS, RALLYING BEHIND A STARRY-EYED CHILD. DID YOU SERIOUSLY THINK -- ANY OF YOU --
-- THAT YOU COULD UNSEAT ME?
WE AGREED TO NOTHING, ZEMO. WE WERE MERELY LISTENING. BUT REALLY, IT WOULDN'T BE THAT HARD TO DEFEAT YOU --
-- YOU HAVE NO POWERS, AFTER ALL.
MY BRAIN IS MY POWER, TRAITRESS. AND NO MATTER WHAT YOU THINK --
-- I AM MORE THAN YOUR EQUAL. I WOULD BE A FOOL TO TRUST YOU, TO FAIL TO PREPARE FOR YOU TURNING AGAINST ME.
AND HELMUT, 13th BARON ZEMO --
SNEK
-- IS NO FOOL!
THERE'S NO BUILDUP, NO SENSE OF SOMETHING BEGINNING. JUST ONE MOMENT, THEY FEEL FINE --
-- AND THE NEXT, PAIN RIPS THROUGH THEM, LIKE THEIR SPINES HAVE BEEN TURNED TO MOLTEN LAVA, LIKE THEIR FLESH IS BEING SEARED FROM WITHIN.
AND WORSE -- IT FEELS LIKE IT'LL NEVER STOP...

I HAD TECHNO PREPARE THIS.
IT ACTS ON JOLT'S AND YOUR INTERNAL ENERGY FIELDS, MOONSTONE -- AND ON THE CIRCUITRY OF THE OTHER TWO.
CLEVER, Hmm?
YOU KNOW... ZEMO... I DIDN'T... TRUST YOU... EITHER...
AND ONCE... I FOUND THE SCHEMATICS... FOR YOUR "AGONIZER"...
...I HAD MACH-1...
KLIK
-- MAKE A JAMMER FOR IT!
CLEVER, Hmm?
...
YOU'RE MORE RESOURC FUL THAN I GAV YOU CREDIT FOR WOMAN. VERY WELL --
-- WE'LL DO THIS THE HARD WAY. GOLIATH, TECHNO --
-- KILL THEM!
H-huh?
KILL US?!
ATLAS HESITATES FOR THE MEREST SECOND. TECHNO DOESN'T. AND IN MOMENTS --

WHAMM
THAT'S IT, JOLT -- DODGE!
YES, MELISSA -- KILL YOU!
KLANG
DID YOU THINK YOU COULD BETRAY ME AND LIVE?
KRAMM
I HAVEN'T REALLY HAD A CHANCE --
-- TO TEST OUT THE COMBAT CAPABILITIES OF MY NEW BODY!
YOU'RE REALLY SOLD ON THAT NEW BODY, TECHNO! WELL, LET ME TELL YOU -- YOU'VE GOT THE FULL OPTIONS PACKAGE AND ALL --
-- BUT YOU DON'T HAVE THE MOVES!
UHH!
KZATT
I SUPPOSE THIS WAS INEVITABLE -- NONE OF YOU ARE SUITED TO BE RULERS BUT MOONSTONE, AND SHE'S NOT TRUST-WORTHY.
AND SINCE THAT'S THE CASE, BETTER TO END THINGS SOONER THAN LATER!
M-MY SOUND-SHIELD!

UP, SONGBIRD!
YOU'RE THINKING OF THIS GUY AS A FRIEND -- AND IT'S PUTTING YOU OFF-STRIDE! BUT HE'S NO FRIEND!
HE WAS GOING TO TURN ON US ALL ALONG, AS SOON AS HE WAS FINISHED USING US! HE JUST ADMITTED IT!
HE'S JUST LIKE ALL THE OTHER LOW-LIFES THAT JERKED ME AROUND OVER THE YEARS! ONLY THIS LOWLIFE'S GONNA DIE!
SORRY, MACH-1 -- BUT I CAN'T LET YOU DO THAT!
KTHUD
UFF!
ATLAS! HOW CAN YOU DO THIS -- HOW CAN YOU HELP HIM?!
BECAUSE HE'S A GOOD SOLDIER, BEETLE! BECAUSE HE'S THE SMART ONE! HE KNOW HIS PLACE, AND KNOWS THAT LOYALTY WILL BE REWARDED!
ONCE THE WORLD IS SUBJUGATED, HE CAN HAVE ANYTHING HE CHOOSES --
-- EVEN THE RIORDAN WOMAN, IF HE STILL WANTS HER!
BKKOW
NOT SO SMUG NOW -- Eh, MOONSTONE?
YOU KNOW, TECHNO --

-- ABE'S RIGHT! I DON'T WANT TO FIGHT FRIENDS -- AND THAT RATTLED ME!
BUT YOU'RE NO MORE MY FRIEND THAN THE ELEMENTS OF DOOM OR THAT ASGARDIAN MONSTER! AND I COULD FIGHT THEM --
-- SO I CAN FIGHT YOU!
WRAMM
TROUBLE IS SONGBIRD -- YOU CAN'T HURT ME!
SAY, MAYBE YOU'LL BE MY REWARD, ONCE THE WORLD'S CONQUERED! MAYBE I'LL PICK YOU!
I DON'T HAVE A HUMAN BODY ANYMORE -- BUT THAT DOESN'T HAVE TO STOP US--!
AND, TWO BULK-HEADS AWAY...
THERE, THAT TAKES CARE OF TECHNO'S PRECIOUS CLOAKING MODULE.
THINGS DIDN'T GO EXACTLY AS I'D PLANNED -- BUT THE GENERAL IDEA WAS TO DISTRACT ZEMO AND TECHNO WHILE I SLIPPED OUT OF THERE --
-- AND THAT PART, AT LEAST, WORKED!
NOW I GUESS I'D BETTER GET BACK TO THE BATTLE, BEFORE THEY NOTICE I'M --
KRGGH
Oh.
NEVER MIND.

THE BATTLE RAGES FOR WHAT SEEMS LIKE AN ETERNITY, THROUGH THE CHAMBERS AND THE CORRIDORS OF THE SPACE STATION.
AT TIMES, IT SEEMS AS IF ZEMO'S FACTION IS UNDEFEATABLE --
FIRE ALL YOU WANT, MACH-1. YOU AREN'T HURTING ME -- AND YOU'RE NOT GOING TO!
KAKATT
FALL, BLAST IT -- WHY WON'T YOU FALL?!
-- AND AT OTHERS, AS IF VICTORY IS ONLY A STROKE OF LUCK AWAY --
NOWHERE TO DODGE, ZEMO. YOU'RE MINE! AND IF I CAN TAKE YOU OUT --
-- GOLIATH AND TECHNO WILL BE LEADERLESS, YES. SO COME AHEAD, CHILD -- AND SEE IF YOU'RE UP TO THE TASK!
BUT EVENTUALLY, THE TIDE TURNS ONE LAST TIME. AND WHEN IT DOES --
10,000 VOLTS, SONGBIRD. LET'S SEE YOUR SOUND-SHIELDS HANDLE THAT!
ZZAKKK
AIIAAAAH!
WH--?
SONGBIRD! MELISSA! ARE YOU ALL R--
KLOK
--AGGKH!
YOU DON'T GET DISTRACTED IN BATTLE, MACH-1 -- YOU CAN'T AFFORD TO. YOU SHOULD KNOW THAT.
-- IT TURNS IRREVOCABLY.

THE REMAINING REBELS DO THEIR BEST TO REGAIN THE MOMENTUM --
KRAK
GLOATING'S PRETTY STUPID TOO, ATLAS!
NOW, ZEMO!
NOW IT'S YOU AND ME -- AND WE'LL SEE WHETHER YOUR ARROGANCE CAN BEAT MY POWERS!
ALAS, CHILD --
-- BUT IT'S NOT TO BE.
H-Huh?
-- WE WON'T. NOT NOW, NOT EVER.
TECHNO! YOU DIRTY--!
SORRY, KID. BUT IF YOU WERE LOOKING FOR A FAIR FIGHT --
-- YOU CAME TO THE WRONG PLACE.
YOUR COMPANIONS ARE ALL DOWN, MOONSTONE. YOU'RE ALONE, AGAINST ALL OF US.
I'LL GIVE YOU ONE CHANCE -- SURRENDER NOW, AND I'LL BE MERCIFUL. DO YOU YIELD?
THAT'S WHAT YOU SAID TO EVERYONE ON EARTH A LITTLE WHILE AGO. WELL, ZEMO --

-- YOU CAN CRAM YOUR MERCY!
HER VOICE IS RAW, ROUGH AND UGLY. ALL HER SOPHISTICATION, ANY HINT OF CONTROL, IS STRIPPED AWAY.
ALL THAT'S LEFT IS RAGE, RAGE... AND POWER.
THIS IS WHAT IT ALWAYS COMES DOWN TO, Eh? FORCE VERSUS FORCE. KILL HER, TECHNO.
TRUST ME, BARON -- SHE'S TOAST.
NO!
THE FORCE OF THE BLAST SLAMS HER BACKWARD, LIKE FLOTSAM STRUCK BY A TIDAL WAVE. BUT SHE REFUSES TO YIELD TO IT, REFUSES TO DROP.
SHE RIGHTS HERSELF, AND SLOWLY, PAINFULLY, BEGINS TO MOVE FORWARD. HER ARMOR BUCKLES, THEN SHREDS. HER SKIN STARTS TO BLISTER.
BUT SHE WON'T FALL, SHE WON'T GIVE THEM THE SATISFACTION. SHE THRUSTS HERSELF FORWARD, AND THEN FORWARD AGAIN.
HOW'S THIS...FOR TOAST, TECHNO? HOW'S THIS... YOU MISERABLE LITTLE... PUKE?
EVER HAD TOAST... THAT...WRAPPED ITS HANDS AROUND YOUR SCRAWNY NECK...AND POPPED YOUR HEAD OFF... LIKE A BOTTLE CAP?
Huh? DID YOU?
INVOLUNTARILY, ZEMO TAKES A STEP BACK. SHE MIGHT MAKE IT AFTER ALL. SHE'S STILL ADVANCING, SLOWER THAN EVER BUT ONLY INCHES AWAY --
-- AND THEN --
Huh?
Eh?
WHAT IN --?

ALL RIGHT! MY PLAN WORKED!
WHAT?
WH-WHO?
WHUH-Oh!
Hmmm.
WELL, WELL, WELL. FUN AND... GAMES.
YOU KNOW...I NEVER THOUGHT I'D BE...GLAD TO SEE SO MANY SUPER HEROES AT THE...SAME TIME. BUT JUST THIS ONCE...

...I'M WILLING TO MAKE AN EXCEPTION!
ARE YOU, MOONSTONE? ARE YOU REALLY? TAKE ANOTHER LOOK AT THEM -- A CLOSE LOOK. LOOK AT THEIR EYES.
THE BIO-MODEM, MOONSTONE.
WE GOT THEM BEFORE THEY EVER DOCKED -- BEFORE THEY SET FOOT ON THIS SATELLITE.
THEY'RE EARTH'S MIGHTIEST HEROES, ALL RIGHT -- BUT THEY'RE MINE.
MINE!
NEXT: THE SHOWDOWN YOU'VE BEEN WAITING FOR!
(BUT -- WHICH SIDE ARE YOU GONNA ROOT FOR, HMM?)

BAGLEY
+
VR

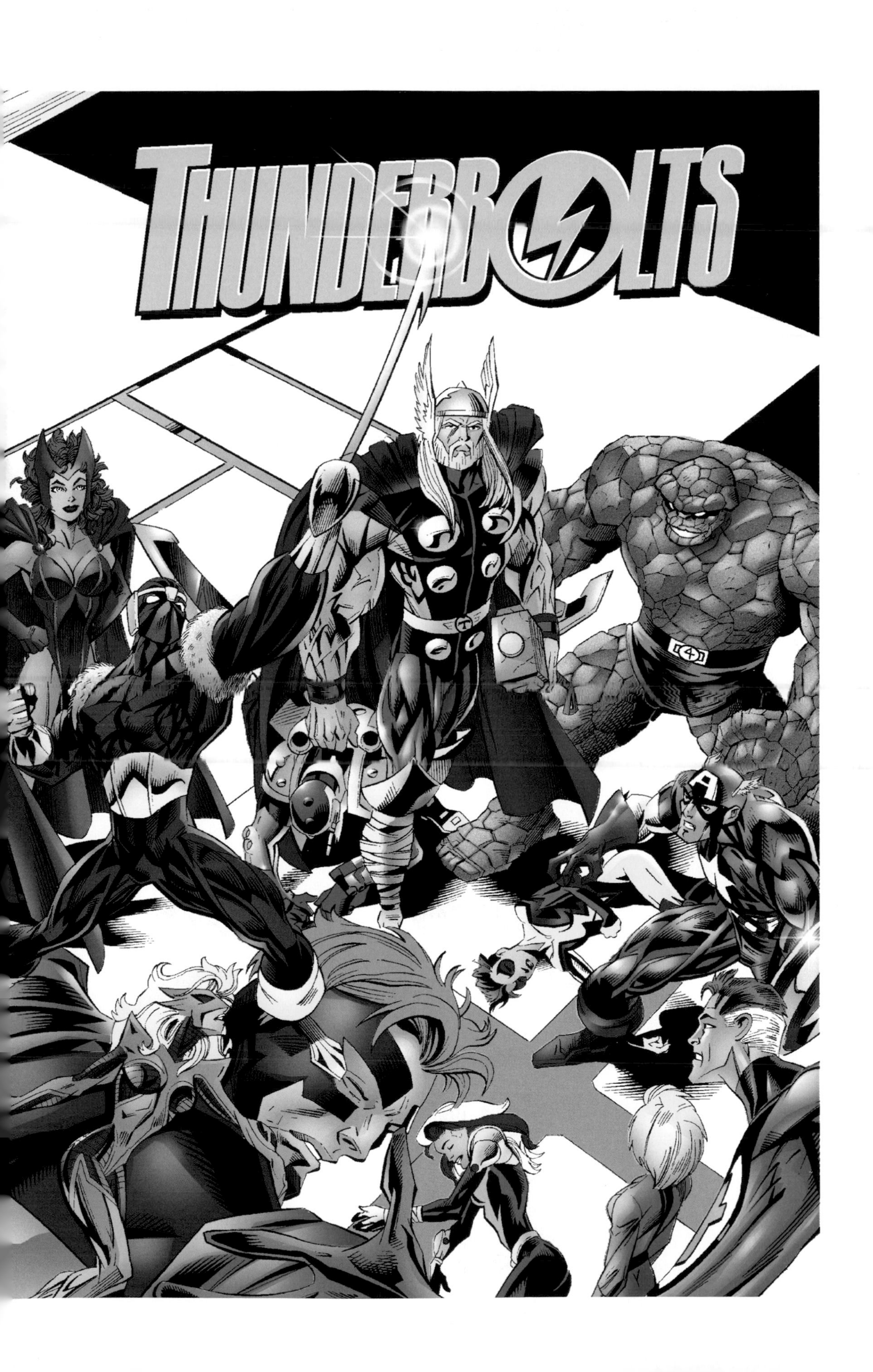
THUNDERBOLTS

Stan Lee presents: JUSTICE LIKE LIGHTNING
ENDGAME
PICTURE OF A MAN TRIUMPHANT.
HIS NAME IS HELMUT, THIRTEENTH BARON ZEMO. HE IS THE SON OF ONE OF THE GREATEST NAZI WAR CRIMINALS IN HISTORY. AND TODAY --
-- TODAY HE IS ON THE VERGE OF RULING THE WORLD.
SO THIS IS VICTORY. THIS IS WHAT IT FEELS LIKE. Ahh, FATHER --
HERE, IN A SATELLITE HIGH ABOVE THE EARTH, HE COMMANDS HIS ARMIES BELOW, PIPING A "BIOLOGICAL MODEM" SIGNAL THROUGH GOVERNMENT, MILITARY AND POLICE COMPUTERS WORLDWIDE --
-- TAKING POSSESSION OF THE MINDS OF THE WORLD'S LEADERS, AND ORCHESTRATING REMOTE-CONTROL COMBAT AS IF IT WERE NOTHING MORE THAN A PUPPET SHOW.
HERE, HE WATCHES, AS COUNTRY AFTER COUNTRY FALLS TO HIM.
HERE, HE HAS JUST FACED DOWN AN INSURRECTION IN THE RANKS OF HIS FOLLOWERS AND TRIUMPHED.
AND HERE, POSSIBLY SWEETEST OF ALL --

-- HE HAS CAPTURED THE MINDS OF EARTH'S MIGHTIEST SUPER HEROES -- THE FAR-FAMED AVENGERS AND THE FANTASTIC FOUR --
-- CAPTURED THEM AS THEY RACED TO THEIR PLANET'S RESCUE, AND TURNED THEM FROM BITTER ENEMIES --
Ah, MOONSTONE -- OR SHOULD I SAY METEORITE, SINCE YOU SEEM TO HAVE CHOSEN TO PLAY YOUR HEROIC ROLE FOR REAL.
YOU COULD HAVE BEEN A QUEEN. YOU COULD HAVE FELT THE THRILL OF ULTIMATE POWER, RATHER THAN BEING SUBJECTED TO IT.
GET ON WITH IT, ZEMO. WE'RE NOT INTERESTED IN ANYTHING YOU HAVE TO SAY.
DEFIANT TO THE LAST, eh? SO TENSE, SO ANGRY -- AND YET YOU DARE NOT ATTACK, KNOWING YOU'LL BE TORN TO BITS BY MY SERVANTS IF YOU DO.
I SUPPOSE I COULD ENSLAVE YOUR MINDS AS WELL -- BUT TO SHOW MERCY WOULD BE TO ALLOW HOPE.

-- INTO NOTHING MORE THAN UNTHINKING, UTTERLY LOYAL SLAVES.
-- IF ONLY YOU COULD SHARE IN THIS.
NOW ALL THAT REMAINS IS TO DECIDE THE FATE OF HIS ONE-TIME FOLLOWERS, THE VILLAINS-MASQUERADING-AS-HEROES THAT THE WORLD KNEW AS THE THUNDERBOLTS.
ATLAS AND TECHNO STAYED LOYAL TO HIM. BUT MACH-1, JOLT, SONGBIRD AND METEORITE --
AND I CAN'T HAVE THAT. NO, YOU'LL HAVE TO DIE -- TO BE EXECUTED BY MY OWN HAND. AND THE FIRST OF YOU TO FALL --
-- WILL BE JOLT. YOUR CHIRPY ADOLESCENT IDEALISM AND GOOD HUMOR HAVE GRATED ON ME SINCE MOONSTONE INVEIGLED YOU ONTO THE TEAM.
IT WILL BE A PLEASURE TO STILL YOUR IRRITATINGLY CHEERFUL TONGUE FOREVER.
DO IT, ZEMO. MAYBE I'LL BE DEAD -- BUT YOU'LL STILL BE A JERK.

SUCH SPIRIT.
IF ONLY I COULD ALLOW MYSELF THE LUXURY OF BREAKING YOU. BUT NO.
HIS GLOVED HAND TIGHTENS ON THE TRIGGER --
-- BUT --
WHRAK
NO! YOU WON'T KILL HER!
ATLAS!
Eh?!
NONE SHALL HARM THE MASTER!
YOU WILL PAY FOR YOUR EFFRONTERY!
OH, YEAH?
WELL, LET ME TELL YOU SOMETHING, GIANT-MAN! YOU MAY BE THE ORIGINAL GROWIN' GUY IN THIS WORLD --
--BUT YOU'LL NEVER -- NEVER -- HAVE THE COMBAT EXPERIENCE I'VE HAD! AND THAT MEANS --
ENOUGH!
NO MORE DELAYS! KILL THEM MY MINIONS -- KILL THEM ALL!

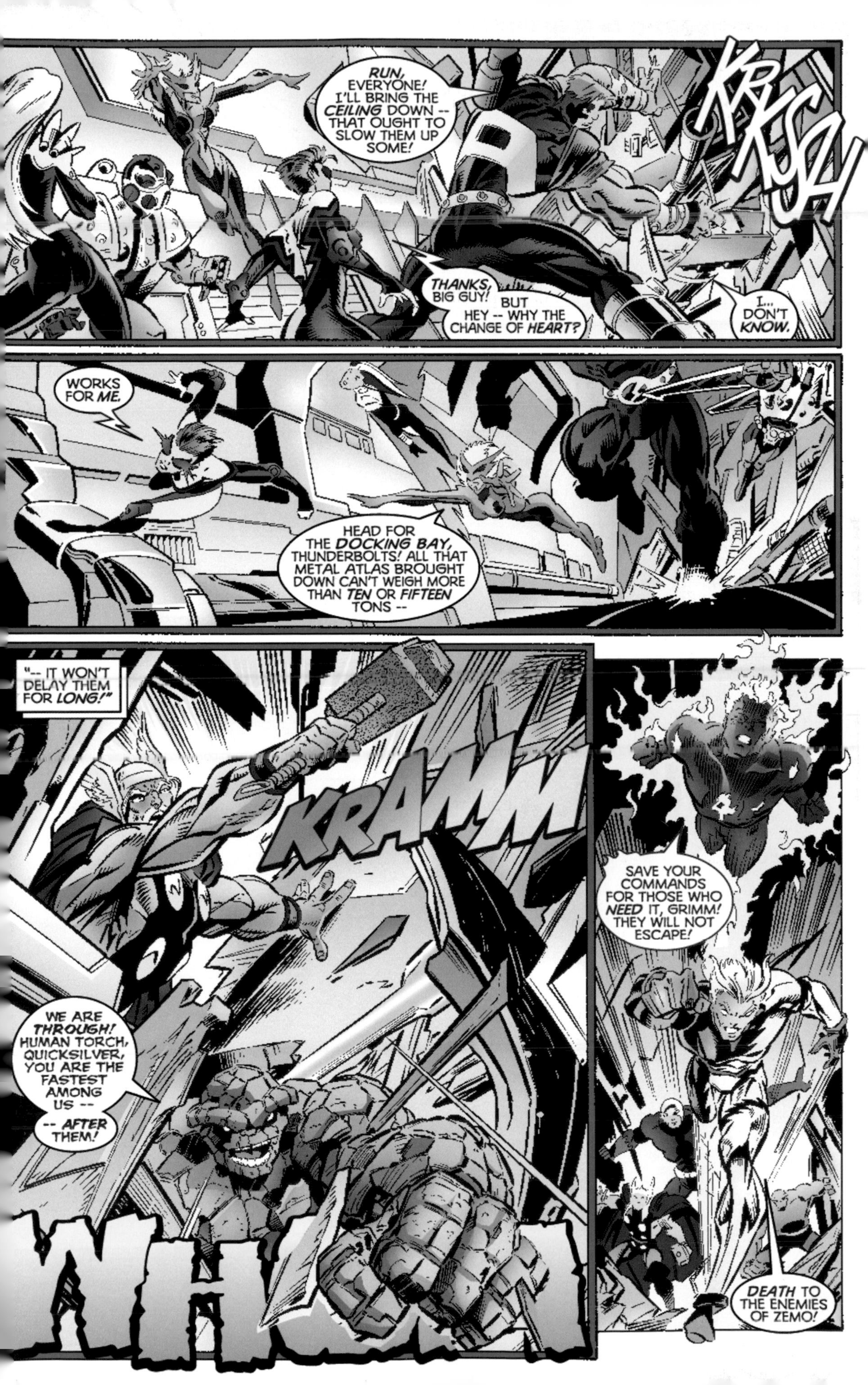
KRKSSH
RUN, EVERYONE! I'LL BRING THE CEILING DOWN -- THAT OUGHT TO SLOW THEM UP SOME!
THANKS, BIG GUY!
BUT HEY -- WHY THE CHANGE OF HEART?
I... DON'T KNOW.
WORKS FOR ME.
HEAD FOR THE DOCKING BAY, THUNDERBOLTS! ALL THAT METAL ATLAS BROUGHT DOWN CAN'T WEIGH MORE THAN TEN OR FIFTEEN TONS --
"-- IT WON'T DELAY THEM FOR LONG!"
KRAMM
WE ARE THROUGH! HUMAN TORCH, QUICKSILVER, YOU ARE THE FASTEST AMONG US --
-- AFTER THEM!
SAVE YOUR COMMANDS FOR THOSE WHO NEED IT, GRIMM! THEY WILL NOT ESCAPE!
DEATH TO THE ENEMIES OF ZEMO!

DEATH!
KROOM KROOM
HEADS UP, TEAM!
I CAN COLLAPSE THE LENGTH OF THE CORRIDOR -- KEEP ANY BUT THESE TWO FROM GETTING THROUGH -- BUT WE'VE GOT TO TAKE THEM OUT QUICKLY!
"QUICKLY?" IF SPEED IS WHAT YOU NEED, WOMAN, YOU ARE DOOMED -- FOR NONE CAN MATCH THE SPEED OF QUICK-SILVER!
KRAC
HUHH!
AW, NUTS!
THIS IS THE HUMAN TORCH? I THOUGHT HE'D BE -- I DON'T KNOW, SCARIER THAN THIS. BUT I'M BLOCKING HIS BLASTS EASILY!
PFAH! I HAVE ALL THE POWER TO HUMBLE ALL OF YOU -- AND ROAST YOU ALIVE!
FRAM
FROOM
I SEE WHAT YOU MEAN, SONGBIRD! I'VE FOUGHT HIM A FEW TIMES...
...AND HE WAS ALWAYS FASTER THAN THIS!
ZEMO'S CONTROLLING HIM WITH THE BIO-MODEM, MACH-1 -- AND IT MUST BE DULLING HIS REFLEXES!
IF SO, WE'VE GOT A CHANCE!

JOLT! TAKE QUICKSILVER -- EVEN IN HIS CURRENT STATE, YOU'RE THE ONLY ONE WHO CAN HANDLE HIM!
GOTCHA!
YOU REALLY THINK YOU CAN OUTRUN ME, GIRL?
NOPE -- AND I BET I COULDN'T EVEN TOUCH YOU IF YOU WERE IN CONTROL! BUT I DON'T NEED TO -- I'VE JUST GOT TO SEE WHERE YOU'RE GOING --
-- AND INTERCEPT YOU!
AKH!
FRAKAM
GOOD! AND NOW THAT HE'S DOWN --
-- I CAN TAKE OUT THE OTHER ONE!
FINE, FINE. GOLD STARS ALL AROUND.
NOW CAN WE GET OUT OF HERE, BEFORE --
-- HUH?!
Oh, MAN -- THE WALL! SOMEBODY TELL ME I'M HALLUCINATING -- THAT THAT'S NOT TECHNO! SOMEBODY TELL ME QUICK!
Oh, COME NOW, ATLAS. YOU'VE KNOWN I CAN MERGE WITH MACHINERY EVER SINCE I SWITCHED TO MY MECHANICAL BODY --
-- SO WHY SO SURPRISED THAT I CAN MANIFEST ANYWHERE WITHIN THAT MACHINERY THAT I CHOOSE?

THEY TURN, THEN --
-- AND FLEE FROM WHAT WAS ONCE THEIR TEAMMATE -- FLEE FOR THEIR LIVES --
HAHAHAHAHAHAHA!
-- AND TECHNO'S LAUGHTER FOLLOWS THEM, ECHOING OFF THE COLD STEEL OF THE CORRIDOR...
SHORTLY...
HERE WE ARE! BUT WHERE'S THE THUNDERJET?!
NO TIME TO LOOK FOR IT -- NOT WHEN TECHNO COULD OVERRIDE THE AIRLOCK CONTROL AT ANY MOMENT!
EVERY-ONE INTO THE QUINJET -- AFTER WHAT I'VE READ ABOUT 'EM IN THE AVENGERS FILES, I THINK I CAN FLY IT!
MOMENTS LATER, AS THE THUNDERBOLTS HOLD THEIR BREATH IN HOPE, THE OUTER AIRLOCK DOORS SLIDE BACK, AND --
SHOOM
WE -- WE MADE IT! WE'RE OUT!
BUT -- WHY DIDN'T TECHNO TRY TO STOP US? WE COULDN'T HAVE BEATEN HIM TO THE --
HUH? WHAT NOW?
-- OH. SO THAT'S WHAT HE WAS DOING.

HAHAHAHAHAHAHAHA!
IMPRESSIVE ISN'T IT? I SWEAR -- THERE'S NO LIMIT TO WHAT I CAN DO WITH THIS BODY -- NONE AT ALL!
I JUST WANTED TO WISH YOU GOOD LUCK, THUNDERBOLTS -- AFTER ALL, YOU'LL NEED IT!
THE EARTH IS 47% ZEMO'S -- AND WITHIN THREE DAYS, IT'LL ALL BE HIS! SO WHERE ARE YOU GOING TO RUN TO -- WHERE CAN YOU HIDE?
THINK ON IT, THUNDERBOLTS -- AND ASK YOURSELVES --
-- HOW MUCH AIR DO YOU HAVE IN THAT QUINJET?
AND IN THE SHIP, THE THUNDERBOLTS EYE EACH OTHER NERVOUSLY, THEN TURN AWAY, UNABLE TO MEET EACH OTHERS' GAZE.
ALL OF THEM BUT JOLT JOINED ZEMO FOR PERSONAL GAIN -- FOR MONEY, FOR POWER, FOR RESPECT --
-- AND FOR A BRIEF MOMENT, THEY HAD EVERYTHING THEY WANTED, AND MORE.
BUT NOW THEY SKIM OVER THE EARTH, SEEING FLASHES OF LIGHT THAT INDICATE BATTLE ZONES BELOW --
-- AND THEY CAN'T DENY IT ANY LONGER. THEY'VE LOST EVERYTHING.
THERE ARE NO OPTIONS -- NOTHING THEY CAN DO, NOWHERE TO GO --

WAIT A MINUTE!
THERE IS SOMEWHERE WE CAN GO! IT WAS MENTIONED IN THE AVENGERS FILES! HOLD ONTO YOUR HATS, T-BOLTS -- WE'RE TRAVELING!
THE QUINJET BANKS UPWARD AND TO STARBOARD -- AND SETS A NEW COURSE, FOR JUST BEYOND THE HORIZON IN FRONT OF THEM.
AND INSIDE...
FLYING QUINJETS, FINDING SANCTUARIES -- YOU'VE BEEN READING THE AVENGERS FILES A LOT, MACH-1...
...WHICH IS ODD, SINCE TECHNO WOULDN'T LET ME NEAR THEM...
YOU'VE JUST GOT TO KNOW HOW TO HANDLE HIM, METEORITE. HE DOESN'T TRUST YOU -- BUT HE'S TOO DISMISSIVE TO BOTHER WORRYING ABOUT ME.
WHEN I WAS HELPING HIM WITH DECRYPTING THE FILES, I PROGRAMMED IN A BACK DOOR TO ALLOW ME PRIVATE ACCESS --
-- AND TECHNO DIDN'T EVEN THINK TO SUSPECT IT.
AND I GUESS HE WAS RIGHT. I MEAN, I WASN'T PLOTTING AGAINST HIM, OR ANY-THING -- I JUST LIKED READING THE CASEFILES.
ESPECIALLY THE ONE ON THAT TIME I BEAT CAPTAIN AMERICA...
EVENTUALLY...
HERE WE ARE, FOLKS -- SAMAROBRYN STATION.
BUILT BY EGGHEAD AS PART OF SOME RANSOM SCAM -- IT WAS REFITTED AND REBUILT BY THE AUTHORITIES AS A WEATHER STATION --
-- AND THE AVENGERS STILL HAD SOME TROUBLE WITH IT.
SO, OKAY, I'LL ADMIT IT LOOKS A LITTLE DORKY -- BUT AT LEAST IT'LL KEEP US ALIVE!
AT A SIGNAL FROM THE QUINJET, SAMAROBRYN'S AIRLOCK SLIDES OPEN --

-- AND MOMENTS LATER...
ABE, YOU'RE A GENIUS! BUT -- HOW LONG CAN WE LAST, EVEN HERE? IF IT'S AN ABANDONED STATION --
IT'S NOT.
THEY KEEP SENDING METEOROLOGICAL MISSIONS UP HERE, USING IT MAYBE EIGHT MONTHS OUT OF THE YEAR.
NO ONE'S HERE NOW -- BUT IT'S FULLY STOCKED WITH AIR AND SUPPLIES -- FOOD PASTE, PROBABLY, BUT I'M NOT COMPLAINING.
NOR I, MACH-1 -- BUT THIS IS A TEMPORARY MEASURE AT BEST. WE CAN RELAX, CATCH OUR BREATH...
...BUT WE'RE STILL GOING TO HAVE TO FIGURE OUT WHAT TO DO NEXT.
Huh?
WHAT DO YOU MEAN, "WHAT TO DO NEXT?"
WE'RE GOING TO GO AFTER ZEMO -- THAT'S WHAT WE'RE GOING TO DO!
CALM DOWN, HALLIE -- AND BE REASONABLE --
IT'D BE A SUICIDE MISSION, KID. NO CHANCE.
WE JUST GOT OUT OF THERE WITH OUR LIVES -- AND YOU WANT TO TURN AROUND AND GO BACK?
I DON'T BELIEVE THIS! MAYBE I WAS WRONG WHEN I THOUGHT YOU GUYS WERE HEROES -- MAYBE I FELL FOR YOUR POSE...
...BUT THIS GOES BEYOND THAT! THIS ISN'T A MATTER OF CHOICE! WHETHER WE STOP ZEMO BECAUSE IT'S THE RIGHT THING TO DO...
...OR BECAUSE WE'VE GOT FRIENDS AND FAMILY DOWN THERE, OR JUST BECAUSE WE WANT AN EARTH TO LIVE ON...
...WE'VE GOT TO DO IT! WE'VE JUST GOT TO! CAN'T YOU SEE THAT?
WELL... CAN'T YOU?
WHEN YOU PUT IT THAT WAY...
I... I GUESS...

IRON MAN!
YOU HAVE NO IDEA HOW GLAD I AM TO HEAR YOU SAY THAT...
WHAT?
HUH?
WHO?
THEY THOUGHT THEY WERE SAFE.
THEY THOUGHT THEY'D ESCAPED FROM ZEMO AND ALL HIS THRALLS -- ESPECIALLY THEIR OLD ENEMIES IN THE AVENGERS.
THEY THOUGHT THEY WERE ALONE -- ONLY TO FIND OUT THAT WASN'T TRUE. SO IT'S UNDERSTANDABLE, PERHAPS, THAT THEIR FIRST REACTION IS --
BRAKKAKKKKA
GET HIM! QUICKLY -- BEFORE HE CAN ATTACK!
YOU DON'T HAVE TO SAY IT TWICE, MACH-1! TRUST ME --
-- HE'S GOT!

ZKAM
ZKAM
TING
SPANG
TING
Oh, PLEASE.
MAYBE YOU GOT TO BE THE GOLDEN BOYS FOR A WHILE, AS THE THUNDERBIRDS OR THUNDERCATS OR WHATEVER IT WAS --
-- BUT LET'S GET SOMETHING STRAIGHT. UNDERNEATH IT ALL, YOU'RE NOTHING BUT TWO-BIT LOSERS, SUCKING UP TO ANY CRIMELORD THAT'LL HAVE YOU --
-- AND I'M IRON MAN.
SEE?
KRSSH
IRON MAN HITS HARD, HIS SKULL RATTLED THROUGH HIS HELMET, AND HIS GYROS MOMENTARILY OFF-LINE.
UHH
STOP IT! YOU STAY AWAY FROM THEM, YOU HEAR ME? YOU STAY AWAY FROM THEM!
AND AS HE STRUGGLES TO HIS FEET, ALL HE CAN THINK IS --
THAT... THAT WAS SCREAMING MIMI?
SCREAMING MIMI?
YEAH, SHE'S NOT WHAT YOU REMEMBER, HUH? NONE OF US ARE!
SO LETS YOU AND ME TALK ABOUT THAT "TWO-BIT LOSER" CRACK...

STOP!
AKH!
AHH!
SETTLE DOWN, ALL OF YOU! IRON MAN'S NOT UNDER ZEMO'S CONTROL -- OR HE WOULDN'T BE HERE ALONE! ZEMO LIKES BLITZKRIEGS TOO MUCH.
YOUR MIND'S YOUR OWN, IRON MAN -- RIGHT?
YES.
MY ARMOR -- OR MY MIND -- HAS BEEN TAKEN OVER A LITTLE TOO OFTEN IN THE PAST TO SUIT ME...
...SO I BUILT SOME SAFEGUARDS INTO THE SUIT THAT KEPT ME FROM BEING CONTROLLED.
I ACTED LIKE THE OTHERS TO FIND OUT WHAT WAS GOING ON, BUT SLIPPED AWAY AND FOLLOWED YOU WHEN YOU ESCAPED.
I FIGURED ANYONE ZEMO WAS THAT MAD AT MIGHT BE SOME HELP IN TAKING HIM DOWN.
THIS IS GREAT -- THIS IS SO GREAT! WITH AN AVENGER ON OUR SIDE, I KNOW WE'RE GOING TO WIN!
WHAT DO YOU THINK WE SHOULD DO, IRON MAN?
LET'S GET SOMETHING STRAIGHT, MISS. I DON'T LIKE YOUR FRIENDS, AND I DON'T LIKE WHAT YOU DID TO THE WORLD WHILE WE WERE GONE.
THE ONLY REASON I'M HERE IS THAT WE SIX MAY BE EARTH'S ONLY HOPE -- BUT DON'T EXPECT ME TO BE CHEERFUL ABOUT IT.
THAT SAID, YOU KNOW MORE ABOUT HIS PLANS THAN I DO -- WHY DON'T YOU FILL ME IN?

AND SHORTLY...
SO THIS "BIO-MODEM" THAT'S CONTROLLING THE OTHERS -- IT CONTROLS THE HUMAN MIND LIKE IT WAS AN ORGANIC MACHINE?
ANY WAY AROUND IT?
WELL, MACH-1 SNAPPED ZEMO OUT OF ITS CONTROL ONCE -- WHEN THE ENCLAVE USED IT ON US...
TRUE, BUT I CAN'T QUITE SEE SNAPPING, SAY, CAPTAIN AMERICA AWAKE -- ONLY TO FIND HIMSELF FACE-TO-FACE WITH KNOWN FELONS.
NO, HE'D PROBABLY OBJECT TO THAT -- I CAN SEE WHY YOU WOULDN'T CONSIDER YOUR HISTORY AN ASSET RIGHT NOW...
DON'T YOU GET HIGH AND MIGHTY WITH ME, MERCENARY!
YOU LIKE TO COME OFF LIKE SOME TIN-PLATED SAINT, BUT YOU TAKE A PAYCHECK FROM TONY STARK! YOU'RE IN NO POSITION TO --
WHOA, WHOA! REMEMBER, WE'RE ON THE SAME SIDE HERE!
AT LEAST FOR THE MOMENT, ANYWAY!
THERE MUST BE A WAY WE CAN GET AT THE BIO-MODEM -- DISABLE IT.
NOT A CHANCE, KID. TECHNO'S MERGED WITH THE STATION -- HE CAN SHIFT ITS CIRCUITRY AROUND, WHISK THE MODEM AWAY BEFORE WE GET NEAR IT.
I CAN JAM THE SIGNAL, KEEP IT FROM PENETRATING MY HELMET -- AND MAYBE I COULD RIG UP SOMETHING THAT'LL PROTECT THE REST OF YOU --
-- BUT WE CAN'T SHIELD THE ENTIRE WORLD...
SO THE KEY TO IT ALL IS TECHNO. WE CAN'T DO ANYTHING WITHOUT TAKING HIM OUT FIRST.
MAYBE, MAYBE NOT. I'VE GOT AN IDEA WHAT WE COULD DO, IF MACH-1 AND IRON MAN CAN FIND A WAY TO GET US IN SAFELY...
YEAH? WHAT IS IT?

WELL, THE THING IS -- IT'S KINDA RISKY...
JOLT EXPLAINS HER PLAN...
...AND FOR THE NEXT FEW HOURS, AT LEAST, THERE IS LITTLE FOR MOST OF THE TEAM TO DO.
THEIR IMMEDIATE FUTURE, AND THAT OF THE WORLD, RESTS ON THE EFFORTS OF TWO MEN -- TWO UNLIKELY PARTNERS --
NICE WORK, BEETLE -- ER, JENKINS. I MAY NOT CARE FOR YOU PERSONALLY -- BUT I'VE GOT TO ADMIT, YOU'RE A GOOD MAN IN THE LAB.
I WOULDN'T HAVE EXPECTED THAT.
SAME BACK AT YOU, IRON MAN. I GUESS YOU MUST HAVE PICKED UP A THING OR TWO FROM TONY STARK, HUH?
IT'S FUNNY. I HAVEN'T HAD MUCH CHANCE TO USE THEM -- BUT WHAT GOT ME INTO THIS GAME IN THE FIRST PLACE WAS MY ENGINEERING SKILLS.
I WAS A HERO. I WAS RESPECTED. LOOKED UP TO. APPLAUDED.
YEAH, MY ENGINEERING SKILLS -- AND THE DESIRE TO BE SOMEONE. TO COUNT FOR SOMETHING. AND NOW LOOK AT ME.
SO IF I MAKE IT THROUGH THIS, DO I GO BACK TO BEING THE BEETLE? TO BEING A CROOK AND A LOSER?
EVEN IF I WANTED TO, COULD I BRING MYSELF TO DO THAT?
ELSEWHERE, SONGBIRD WATCHES EARTH TURN SLOWLY BELOW, AND FINDS HERSELF THINKING ABOUT DEATH. SHE KNOWS HOW RISKY THE PLAN IS.
SHE KNOWS WHAT COULD HAPPEN. AND THE THOUGHT TERRIFIES HER.
BUT NO, SHE TELLS HERSELF. THIS IS WHAT YOU GET FOR LETTING YOURSELF OPEN UP -- FOR LETTING YOURSELF CARE, AND HOPE, AND DREAM.
YOU USED TO BE TOUGH. YOU USED TO BE A GRAPPLER, TO BE SCREAMING MIMI.
YOU USED TO BE A GRAPPLER...

NEARBY, ATLAS PACES, ENDLESSLY CIRCLING THE STATION. HIS THOUGHTS, TOO, KEEP RETURNING TO THE SAME SUBJECT, BUT IN HIS CASE, IT'S...
BETRAYAL. THAT'S ALL MY LIFE AMOUNTS TO, ISN'T IT? I BETRAYED MY SISTER, RUNNIN' OFF AND LETTIN' HER GET KILLED.
I BETRAYED DALLAS BY LYIN' TO HER, LETTIN' HER FALL FOR WHO SHE THOUGHT I WAS. AND I EVEN BETRAYED ZEMO.
HE SAVED MY LIFE, RESCUED ME FROM KOSMOS -- AND HOW DO I REPAY HIM? I HIT HIM FROM BEHIND, BLINDSIDE HIM WHEN HE TRUSTED ME.
BUT I COULDN'T LET HIM KILL JOLT -- IT'D HAVE BEEN LIKE BETRAYIN' LINDY ALL OVER AGAIN. I JUST COULDN'T DO IT.
SO HERE I AM, WORKIN' WITH AN ENEMY TO MAKE AN ASSAULT ON A MAN I OWE MY LIFE TO. I DON'T KNOW WHICH SIDE I'M ON.
I DON'T KNOW WHAT I'M GONNA DO. ALL I KNOW -- IS THAT WHATEVER I DO, I'M GONNA END UP BETRAYIN' SOMEONE. AGAIN.
HIGH ABOVE, IN THE UPPER REACHES OF THE SPACE STATION, JOLT SITS, KICKING HER FEET AND TRYING TO MAKE SENSE OF THINGS.
EVEN NOW, KNOWING THE TRUTH, SHE HAS A TOUGH TIME THINKING OF THEM AS CRIMINALS. ABE, MELISSA -- EVEN ERIK.
SHE KNOWS THEM -- KNOWS THEM AS PEOPLE, AND THAT MAKES IT HARD. BUT THEN, SHE THOUGHT SHE KNEW METEORITE -- MOONSTONE -- TOO.
SHE WAS HER FRIEND, SHE'D THOUGHT. HER PROTECTOR. AND IF SHE WAS THAT WRONG ABOUT HER, COULD SHE BE WRONG ABOUT THE OTHERS?
HOW MUCH OF THIS IS SHE DOING, SHE WONDERS, BECAUSE SHE WANTS TO PROVE SOMETHING --
-- TO BE A HERO, INSTEAD OF JUST AN IDIOT WHO GOT DUPED COMPLETELY --
-- AND HOW MUCH IS JUST THAT SHE'S GOT NOWHERE ELSE TO GO?

NEARBY, IN THE STATION COMMANDER'S PRIVATE QUARTERS...
FLASH
Ahh, THAT'S BETTER!
NOTHING LIKE FRESH CLOTHES TO HELP ME THINK MORE CLEARLY -- AND A NEW UNIFORM SYMBOLIZES NEW STARTS, NEW POSSIBILITIES.
IF I KNOW THE OTHERS, THEY'RE WALLOWING IN THE PAST, IN REGRETS, TRYING TO FIGURE OUT WHO THEY ARE, WHAT THEY WANT TO DO.
BUT I KNOW WHO I AM. I'VE ALWAYS KNOWN.
AND I KNOW THAT IF I'M GOING TO SALVAGE SOMETHING FROM THIS MESS, I NEED TO THINK IT ALL THROUGH COLDLY, AND DECIDE ON MY BEST MOVE.
RIGHT NOW, THAT BEST MOVE LIES WITH JOLT AND IRON MAN --
-- SO THAT'S WHAT I DO. FOR NOW...
AND, BACK IN THE ELECTRONICS LAB...
OKAY, THIS SHOULD DO IT. IT'LL BLOCK RECEPTION OF THE BIO-MODEM SIGNAL IN A 300-YARD RADIUS AROUND IT, FOR MAYBE AN HOUR.
GOOD. I'LL TELL THE OTHERS WE'RE READY.
AS MACH-1 LEAVES, IRON MAN FINDS HIMSELF WONDERING ABOUT THESE THUNDERBOLTS. THEY'RE VILLAINS. HE KNOWS THAT --
-- BUT THEY JUST DON'T SEEM LIKE IT, SOMEHOW. HE COULDN'T SAY WHY, BUT THEY FEEL LIKE SOMETHING MORE TO HIM, SOMETHING DIFFERENT.
AND SOME OF THEM, LIKE THAT JOLT GIRL --
-- THEY DON'T SEEM ALL THAT DIFFERENT FROM PEOPLE HE'S SERVED WITH IN THE AVENGERS...
Ah, CAPTAIN AMERICA.

HERE YOU STAND, GLASSY-EYED AND UNRESISTING -- A PUPPET COMPLETELY IN MY POWER, TO DISPOSE OF HOWEVER I MIGHT WISH.
IT'S AMUSING, ISN'T IT? ONCE, ALL I COULD THINK OF WAS REVENGE -- ALL I WANTED WAS TO KILL YOU AS YOU KILLED MY FATHER.
I KNEW YOU DIDN'T REALLY KILL HIM, OF COURSE --
-- YOU'RE TOO UNWAVERINGLY, UNTHINKINGLY HONEST TO DENY RESPONSIBILITY IF YOU'D ACTUALLY DONE IT.
NO, I ACCEPT NOW THAT MY FATHER CAUSED HIS OWN DEATH -- BUT STILL, I WASTED YEARS OF MY LIFE REFUSING TO ACKNOWLEDGE IT --
-- YEARS IN WHICH I WAS UTTERLY BLIND TO ANYTHING ELSE.
IT TOOK YOUR APPARENT DEATH TO MAKE ME LOOK PAST THAT --
-- TO MAKE ME REALIZE THAT INSTEAD OF SEEKING TO CLEAN UP MY FATHER'S UNFINISHED BUSINESS --
-- I SHOULD INSTEAD FOLLOW IN HIS FOOTSTEPS, AND TAKE MY TRUE PLACE AS A ZEMO -- AS THE RIGHTFUL MASTER OF THE WORLD!
AND NOW, I'VE WON. I RULE THE WORLD -- OR 67% OF IT, ACCORDING TO THE LATEST FIGURES, WITH THE REST TO FOLLOW SOON.
AND IT FEELS GOOD. IT FEELS JUST. IT FEELS... RIGHT.
AND WONDER OF WONDERS, HERE YOU ARE, FALLEN INTO MY HANDS ANYWAY, EVEN THOUGH I HAVE LET MY DESIRE FOR REVENGE GO.
AND WHO AM I TO ARGUE WITH FATE? YOU ARE MY REWARD. MY SIGN --
-- TELLING ME I HAVE MADE THE RIGHT CHOICE.
SO I'LL KILL YOU ANYWAY, AS A SYMBOL. AS A CASTING OFF OF THE PAST, AND THE FINAL ACCEPTANCE OF MY TRUE DESTINY.
YOU WOULD DO ANYTHING FOR ME, WOULD YOU NOT?

I WOULD DO ANYTHING FOR YOU.
STEP INTO THE AIRLOCK.
I WILL CYCLE YOU THROUGH, EXPELLING YOU OUTWARD, TO DIE IN AGONY OF EXPOSURE TO THE VACUUM OF SPACE.
AS YOU COMMAND.
CURIOUS. THIS IS ODDLY UNSATISFYING.
I ALWAYS ASSUMED I WOULD BEAT YOU IN BATTLE, NOT THROUGH ELECTRONIC TRICKERY. BUT NO MATTER -- YOU'LL NONETHELESS --
-- Eh?! THE VIEWPORT?!
ALERT! ALERT! PROXIMITY WARNING -- SHIP APPROACHING! IDENTIFIED AS AVENGERS QUINJET, MODEL EPSILON-5!
TECHNO -- IT MUST BE THE RENEGADES! USE THE BIO-MODEM ON THEM -- QUICKLY!
I CAN'T, BARON -- THEY'RE SHIELDED AGAINST IT. BRACE YOURSELF. IMPACT IS --
-- IMMINENT!
THEY HAVE PENETRATED INTO CARGO HOLD SEVEN, WHERE WE HAVE BEEN STORING EARTH'S HEROES.
SPKA DOOM
WAKE THEM UP, THEN! WAKE UP THE HEROES -- AND KILL MOONSTONE AND HER TRAITOROUS COMPANIONS!
MOMENTARILY, BARON. MY FIRST PRIORITY MUST BE REPAIRING THE HULL BREACH --

KRAM
BUT EVEN AS TECHNO SEALS THE HULL AROUND THE QUINJET...
OKAY, PEOPLE -- YOU KNOW THE PLAN. SO MOVE -- AND FAST!
YOU CAN'T HOPE TO WIN, METEORITE. WHAT DO YOU THINK YOU'RE DOING?
WHAT ARE WE DOING, TECHNO? HEY, WE'RE BIG, BAD SUPER-VILLAINS --
-- WE'RE JUST DOING WHAT COMES NATURALLY!
THE BIO-MODEM JAMMER HITS THE DECK, TRIGGERS, AND...
ZKAKK
EH?
AVENGERS! F.F.! THANK HEAVEN I WAS ABLE TO WAKE YOU!
THE MASTERS OF EVIL HAVE FOUND US -- AND THEY'RE GOING TO KILL US ALL!
WHA--?
THE -- THE MASTERS --?
EVERYTHING -- SO FUZZY --
WE WERE IN THE QUINJET -- AND THEN THERE WAS A COMMUNICATIONS BEACON, AND --
NO OFFENSE, TECHNO --
THIS IS INSANE! YOU'RE COMMITTING SUICIDE -- WHY?

-- BUT THAT'S NOT REALLY ANY OF YOUR BUSINESS ANYMORE, IS IT?
KZAK
IRON MAN WAS RIGHT! THE MASTERS ARE ATTACKING!
BUT -- I SEEM TO REMEMBER -- I THOUGHT --
KRAKAM
YOU THINK TOO MUCH, RICHARDS! THAT MAY HELP YOU OUT A LOT AS LEADER OF THE FANTASTIC FOUR, BUT RIGHT HERE AND RIGHT NOW --
-- ALL IT'S GONNA DO IS GET YOU KILLED, STARTING WITH CHROME-DOME HERE!
KZAK
BRAKKA BRAKKA BRAKKA
OD'S BLOOD! THEY DO ATTACK WITH THE FEROCITY OF HELA'S DARK LEGIONS!
JAN! STAY BACK!
NOT A CHANCE, LOVER! HE TRIED TO KILL YOU -- AND I'M TAKING IT OUT OF HIS HIDE! HE CAN'T DO THAT!
AIN'T YOU HEARD, WASPIE? WE'RE FILTH -- THE SCUM OF THE EARTH!
WE CAN DO WHATEVER WE WANT!

NEARBY...
YOU! YOU ARE FAST, GIRL -- BUT NOT FAST ENOUGH! STILL I CAN'T SHAKE THE FEELING THAT --
THAT WE'VE MET, QUICKSILVER?
BUT THAT'S NOT POSSIBLE, IS IT?
AFTER ALL, IF WE'D MET, I MIGHT HAVE LEARNED ENOUGH ABOUT YOUR FIGHTING STYLE --
-- TO MANAGE TO STAY OUT OF YOUR GRASP!
AND THAT JUST COULDN'T HAPPEN, COULD IT?
BEN! THOR! GRAB HER! IF WE CAN IMMOBILIZE HER --
NOT A CHANCE, RICHARDS!
IT'S WORKING!
KROM
THERE WASN'T A CHANCE TO CLUE THE HEROES IN TO OUR PLAN -- TO WHAT NEEDED TO BE DONE! SO WE HAD TO DEPEND ON THEIR EMOTIONS --
-- GET THEM TO ATTACK US, TO START A BRAWL AS A DISTRACTION TO COVER OUR REAL PLAN! BUT THAT'S ONLY THE START --
"-- AND THE REST IS GOING TO DEPEND ON WHAT HAPPENS IN THE NEXT FEW SECONDS!"
DIE, HUMAN TORCH!
THIS IS SCREWY.
WHY'RE THEY ATTACKING US, WHEN THEY'RE SO OUTNUMBERED?

YEAH -- AND WHAT ARE THEY AFTER, ANYWAY? ALL THIS RUCKUS -- BUT THE MASTERS OF EVIL DON'T JUST FIGHT WITHOUT A PURPOSE.
SOMETHING'S NOT RIGHT HERE...
Uh... OF COURSE IT IS, HAWKEYE! WE'RE ROTTEN PEOPLE -- WHAT MORE EXCUSE DO WE NEED TO TRY TO KILL HEROES?
Uh-Oh.
THEY'RE CATCHING ON -- I KNEW THEY WOULD, BUT I DIDN'T THINK IT'D BE THIS SOON.
IF THE BATTLE ENDS BEFORE --
YOUR MELEE THREATENS THE INTEGRITY OF THIS STATION, INTRUDERS! IT MUST BE HALTED --
--WITH ALL DUE SPEED!
KRANGG
PERFECT!
WE'VE DRAWN TECHNO INTO THE BATTLE! THAT'LL KEEP HIM DISTRACTED -- AND IT'LL PROVIDE MORE ANTAGONISTS TO KEEP THIS BRAWL GOING --
-- WHILE WE GO AFTER THE BIO-MODEM!
SURE ENOUGH, THERE GOES METEORITE, JUST AS PLANNED --
"-- AND JOLT..."
UHH!
THERE, GIRL! YOUR REFLEXES ARE INCREDIBLE --
-- BUT ALL YOUR JUMPING AROUND LIKE A JACKRABBIT COULD ONLY DELAY YOUR CAPTURE, NOT ESCAPE IT!
I HAVE YOU!
YEAH, YEAH, YOU'VE GOT ME, AVENGER --

-- BUT CAN YOU KEEP ME?!
KZAT
UHH!
HATED TO DO THAT TO AN AVENGER -- BUT I HAD TO! IF METEORITE DOESN'T MAKE IT THROUGH, I'M THE ONLY ONE WHO CAN GET TO --
YOU'RE NOT GOING ANYWHERE, YOUNG LADY.
C-CAPTAIN AMERICA?!
THAT WAS A CUTE TRICK YOU PLAYED ON QUICKSILVER -- SOME SORT OF INTERNAL BIO-ELECTRICITY, RIGHT? BUT I WON'T LET YOU TRY IT ON ME.
UHH... WELL, YOU SEE, SIR, IT'S KIND OF AN EMERGENCY, AND I REALLY DON'T HAVE TIME TO --
YOU'VE GOT ALL THE TIME IN THE WORLD, BECAUSE I'M NOT LETTING YOU PAST M--
ZKAM
UHH! REPULSOR RAY -- BUT WHY--?
I'VE GOT A PRETTY GOOD IDEA --
-- BUT LIKE I SAID, I CAN'T STOP TO EXPLAIN! THANKS, IRON MAN -- I'M OUTTA HERE!
HOPE I DIDN'T MESS YOU UP ANY!
SORRY, CAP -- STRAY BLAST! ONE OF THOSE ROBOT THINGS DUCKED OUT OF THE WAY AT THE LAST MINUTE!

ACROSS THE ROOM...
I TOLD YOU I WAS A BETTER FIGHTER THAN YOU, GIANT-MAN! BUT THAT AIN'T ALL! WHEN I GROW LARGER --
-- I GET STRONGER, TOUGHER, MORE BULLET-PROOF! YOU JUST GET STRONGER, AN' IN THIS GAME --
-- THAT'S NOT ENOUGH!
BRAM
THEN PERHAPS, GARGANTUAN ONE --
Huh?
KRAK
-- THOU WOULDST DO BETTER TO CHALLENGE ONE MORE APPROPRIATE TO THY POWER LEVEL!
TH-- UHH!
NICE... NICE SHOT, THOR... BUT I'M NOT... THROUGH YET...
AW, HE WAS JUST SETTIN' YOU UP FER ME, ANYWAYS.
Oh, NO.
OH, YES!
YOU REMEMBER ME, DON'T'CHA? GUY WHO USEDTA LIVE IN FOUR FREEDOMS BEFORE YA? GUY WHO'D BE LIVIN' IN IT NOW --
WHKOW
-- IF YOU HADN'T BLOWN THE WHOLE PLACE TA SMITHER-EENS!

MEANWHILE...
JUST HOLD THEM OFF A LITTLE BIT LONGER, SUE...
...THE TECHNOLOGY HERE ISN'T ANY-THING I DON'T RECOGNIZE --
-- IT'S JUST BEEN ADAPTED IN SOME ASTONISHINGLY INNOVATIVE WAYS!
BUT IF I CAN FIGURE OUT HOW TO TAKE IT OVER --
DON'T WORRY, REED. OUR FRIEND HERE WITH THE LITTLE PINK WINGS HASN'T REALIZED IT YET --
-- BUT NOTHING GETS THROUGH THE NVISIBLE WOMAN'S FORCE-FIELDS. NOTHING!
YOU GOT THAT, MISS?
Oh, REALLY?
WELL, I CAN HEAR YOU, AND YOU CAN HEAR ME -- SO SOUND MUST TRAVEL THROUGH YOUR PRECIOUS FIELD! AND MAKING THINGS OUT OF SOUND --
-- THAT'S LITTLE MIMI'S STOCK-IN-TRADE THESE DAYS!
SO MUCH FOR YOU -- NOW FOR YOUR TAG-TEAM PARTNER...
KLUD
GOT HIM! I THINK THAT'S THE BEETLE, IN HIS NEW BATTLE SUIT, BUT WHOEVER IT IS --
-- HE WON'T BOTHER US ANY MORE!
THE PROBABILITY-WARPING POWERS OF THE SCARLET WITCH CAUSE EVERY CIRCUIT IN MACH-1'S ARMOR TO FAIL AT ONCE --
-- SHUTTING IT DOWN COMPLETELY --

-- AND LEAVING ONLY ONE THUNDERBOLT ACTIVE...
ALL RIGHT, YOUNG LADY -- LET'S DISCUSS WHAT YOU DID TO MY WIFE!
I WAS AFRAID OF THIS. WE KNEW WE WERE OUTNUMBERED, BUT WE DIDN'T HAVE MUCH CHOICE IN THE MATTER.
I'VE GOT TO HELP SONGBIRD, BUT I CAN'T DO IT OPENLY, OR THEY'LL INSTANTLY REALIZE THIS IS A SHAM -- AND SO WILL TECHNO!
AVENGERS! F.F.! I NEED SOME HELP HERE -- FAST!
THESE ROBOTS -- THERE ARE TOO MANY OF THEM! AND MORE ARE TURNING UP ALL THE TIME!
HELP ME TAKE 'EM DOWN -- OR WE'RE LOST!
ABE!
I CAN'T -- I CAN DEAL WITH SOME OF THEM, BUT NOT ALL OF THEM! NOT ALONE!
DON'T WORRY, SHELLHEAD -- WE GOT YOUR BACK!
GREAT, GREAT.
TECHNO'S RESPONDING TO MY CALL BY MANIFESTING MORE ROBO-BODIES --
-- AND THE OTHERS THINK THAT'S WHAT I WAS WARNING THEM OF!
I DON'T LIKE MISLEADING THEM, BUT WE'VE GOT TO KEEP THE PRESSURE ON --
WHOA!
YOU MUST BE BROUGHT UNDER CONTROL, HEROES -- DEAD OR ALIVE!
THOU ART WELCOME TO TRY!

"-- IF METEORITE AND JOLT ARE TO GET THROUGH!"
COME NO CLOSER, WOMAN! I'M WARNING YOU!
KBLAM KBLAM KBLAM
WHAT'S THIS, BARON?
PTANG
SPING
NO "AGONY INDUCERS"? NO SECRET BACK-UP PLANS? DON'T TELL ME YOU'RE OUT OF DIRTY TRICKS!
YOU ARE?
KRRRNCH
WELL, ISN'T THAT JUST TOO BAD.
NNH!
THE BONES OF BARON ZEMO'S HAND SNAP LIKE TWIGS IN METEORITE'S GRIP.
HIS JAW SHATTERS.
I'LL TELL YOU, BARON. I DID HAVE SOMETHING ELSE TO DO --
SKOW
-- BUT I THINK I'LL ENJOY MYSELF HERE FOR A LITTLE WHILE. AFTER ALL, JOLT'S FAST, AND SHE'S RESOURCEFUL -- I'M SURE SHE CAN HANDLE IT.
AND AT THAT MOMENT, THREE DECKS BELOW...
AHA! THE SIGNAL ROOM -- JUST WHERE MACH-1 SAID IT WOULD BE!
THAT TAKES CARE OF THE ELECTRONIC LOCK, AND --

-- Huh? Oh, NO!
LET ME EXPLAIN SOMETHING, ZEMO. LET ME TELL YOU WHY I UNDERMINED YOUR LEADERSHIP AT EVERY TURN.
I'VE GOT A PRETTY SIMPLE PHILOSOPHY OF LIFE. YOU WANT TO HEAR IT?
THREE OF ZEMO'S INCISORS TURN TO POWDER UNDER HIS MASK.
KRAM
IT'S THIS: DON'T. GET. CAUGHT!
HIS RIBS CRUMPLE.
Oh, I WAS STUPID AT FIRST -- I THOUGHT MY POWERS MADE ME INVINCIBLE...
WHUDD
...SO I ENDED UP GETTING A RECORD, GETTING CAUGHT.
I WAS WILLING TO RIDE IT OUT, SERVE MY SENTENCE AND START ANEW -- BUT YOU PRESS-GANGED ME INTO YOUR SCHEME, AND THERE WENT THAT.
STILL, IT WAS A GOOD SCHEME -- POSING AS HEROES -- AND WE MADE IT WORK. WE HAD IT ALL -- PUBLIC SUPPORT, ADULATION --
-- THE PERFECT COVER TO PULL ANY NUMBER OF SCAMS --
-- AND YOU WENT AND BLEW IT, OVER JUST ONE!
PKOW
WHO CARES ABOUT RULING THE WORLD?! WHO WANTS TO DO THAT MUCH WORK?
WE COULD HAVE RUN THIS CON OUT FOR YEARS BEFORE IT GOT OLD! BUT NO, YOU COULDN'T BE SMART --
-- NOT WHEN YOU COULD PLAY HITLER LIKE YOUR IDIOT FATHER!
WELL, IT'S BUNKER TIME, ZEMO. ONLY EVA BRAUN ISN'T AVAILABLE RIGHT NOW, SO YOU'LL HAVE TO SETTLE FOR --

METEORITE! STOP!
PUT HIM DOWN -- OR SUFFER THE CONSEQUENCES!
HAH! YOU THINK I'M WORRIED ABOUT YOU, TECHNO?
YOU'RE THROUGH --YOU JUST DON'T KNOW IT YET. WHY, ANY MOMENT NOW --
Uh METEORITE? WE'VE GOT A LITTLE PROBLEM HERE.
WHAT?!
THE BIO-MODEM -- IT'S GONE! HE MOVED IT!
I AM THIS STATION, METEORITE. IT'S MY BODY NOW. DID YOU REALLY THINK YOU COULD DISTRACT ME FROM WHAT WAS HAPPENING IN IT?
SAY THIS FOR METEORITE -- SHE REACTS SWIFTLY. SHE HESITATES, BUT ONLY FOR A SPLIT SECOND --
-- AND SHE'S ALREADY ACTING, TRYING ANOTHER PLAN...
YOUR BODY. YOU'RE AWFULLY PROUD OF YOUR NEW ROBOTIC STATE, AREN'T YOU? OR COULD YOU JUST BE IN DENIAL, JUST THE TINIEST BIT?
AFTER ALL, YOU HAVEN'T ONCE MENTIONED ANY OF THE DRAWBACKS THAT COME WITH IT --
-- NEVER TO FEEL A WOMAN'S TOUCH...
...NEVER TO KNOW PHYSICAL PLEASURE AGAIN...
I -- I NEVER CARED ABOUT THAT SORT OF THING. YOU KNOW THAT.
BESIDES -- I CAN INVENT WHATEVER I NEED -- INDISTINGUISHABLE FROM THE REAL THING!
BUT YOU'LL KNOW, TECHNO. YOU'LL KNOW IT'S FAKERY, ILLUSION --
-- NOT A REAL HUMAN LOVING YOU, NOT ANYBODY REAL CARING...

I DON'T NEED LOVE, I TELL YOU! I DON'T WANT LOVE -- I NEVER HAVE
ALL I WANT IS RESPECT!
Oh, REALLY?
LET'S JUST SAY THAT'S TRUE, FOR ARGUMENT'S SAKE. ARE YOU EVEN GETTING RESPECT?
YOU'RE KNOWN THE WORLD OVER AS ZEMO'S FLUNKY --
-- WHERE'S THE RESPECT IN THAT?
ALL YOU'VE DONE, EVEN ALL THIS -- WILL BE SEEN AS ZEMO'S TRIUMPH, WITH YOU JUST THE UNDERLING WHO DID THE GRUNT WORK --
-- THE LACKEY WHO GOT HIS HANDS DIRTY.
THAT'S NOT TRUE! I'M NOT A LACKEY!
I HAVE A REPUTATION! I HAVE A TRACK RECORD! PEOPLE KNOW WHAT I CAN DO -- THEY DO!
THEY DO? THEN WHY IS YOUR OLD PARTNER MENTALLO HIGHER ON THE MOST WANTED LISTS THAN YOU ARE?
AND ON EVERY DECK OF THE STATION, ON EVERY VIEW-SCREEN...
YOU'RE LYING! YOU'RE LYING! I'M ACCESSING S.H.I.E.L.D. FILES RIGHT NOW! INTERPOL FILES!
HE'S THIRTY-SEVEN PLACES LOWER ON THE LISTS THAN --
Hmm?
WHAM
KLUD
Oh, I SEE. NOT A BAD STRATEGY, ALL TOLD. A BIT BRUTAL, TRUE, BUT UNDER THE CIRCUMSTANCES...
JOHNNY! IRON MAN! BLAST A TUNNEL THROUGH THE DECKS -- THAT WAY! I LOCATED THE STATION'S CENTRAL PROCESSING UNIT BEFORE, AND --
WHATEVER YOU WANT, REED --

-- YOU GOT IT. WHAT NEXT?
SCARLET WITCH! DOWN THERE!
SOMEONE'S DISTRACTING TECHNO -- METEORITE, POSSIBLY -- GIVING US SECONDS TO ACT! THAT'S HIS BRAIN DOWN THERE, AND --
I GET IT, Dr. RICHARDS. BEFORE HE CAN MOVE IT, OR SHIELD IT --
-- YOU WANT ME TO USE MY HEX POWER TO SCRAMBLE IT!
THERE IS NO AIR IN SPACE TO CARRY THE SOUND OF TECHNO'S SCREAM.
BUT THROUGHOUT THE SATELLITE, IT RINGS LOUDLY, RESONATING FROM THE AUDIBLE TO THE SUBSONIC, AND BEYOND...
...AND THE STATION, ALREADY WEAKENED BY TECHNO'S RESHAPING OF IT, AND THE STRESSES OF THE BATTLE --
-- BEGINS TO FALL APART.
Uhhh... MUSTA... FALLEN THROUGH THE FLOOR...
...GOTTA FIND OTHERS... SEE IF IT'S NOT TOO LATE TO HELP WITH...
JOSTEN.
Huh?

GET... GET UP, JOSTEN. YOUR MASTER... HAS NEED OF YOU.
ZEMO?
HELP... HELP ME REACH THE ESCAPE POD...
BUT -- BUT I --
I... MUST ESCAPE. I MUST LIVE TO HAVE MY REVENGE ON THOSE WHO HAVE... BETRAYED ME. I MUST REGROUP... AND CONQUER ANEW.
YOU OWE ME, JOSTEN. YOU HAVEN'T FORGOTTEN THAT.
OH, MAN.
I'M GOING TO REGRET THIS. I KNOW I AM.
ESCAPE POD-D
THERE -- THERE YOU GO, ZEMO.
GET IN, JOSTEN. I NEED MORE... HELP THAN THIS.
YOU... OWE ME. YOU OWE ME.
UH -- WELL, I --
NO, ZEMO. NO. YOU SAVED MY LIFE. I SAVED YOURS.
WE'RE EVEN.
PTAK
THE ESCAPE POD DISENGAGES SMOOTHLY --
-- AND ATLAS WATCHES IT ARC AWAY, WATCHES IT HEAD FOR EARTH, AND HE WONDERS -- WHO HAS HE BETRAYED THIS TIME?
AND THEN, AS HE WATCHES, JUST FOR A MOMENT --
-- BUT NO, IT COULDN'T HAVE BEEN. HE COULDN'T HAVE SEEN THAT.
IT WAS A TRICK OF THE LIGHT, THAT'S ALL. IT COULDN'T HAVE BEEN --

ATLAS!
QUIT WOOLGATHERING AND GET A MOVE ON! WE'VE GOT TO GET OUT OF HERE --
-- IN CASE YOU HADN'T NOTICED, THE WHOLE PLACE IS COMING APART AT THE SEAMS!
METEORITE! JOLT! THEN -- WE WON?
WHAT ABOUT THE AVENGERS -- THE FANTASTIC FOUR? THEY'RE STILL UP THERE -- HOW ARE THEY GOING TO GET OUT?
LET THEM WORRY ABOUT THEMSELVES, JOLT -- THEY'VE HAD PRACTICE! JUST GET TO THE HANGAR BAY --
"-- AND FIND US A SHIP -- ANY SHIP!"
AND MOMENTS LATER, WITH A FINAL, CONVULSIVE HEAVE --
-- THE SATELLITE THAT ONLY AN HOUR AGO CONTROLLED MORE THAN HALF OF THE WORLD BELOW --
-- CEASES TO EXIST.

A BLUE SPHERE. AGAIN. HOW ODDLY... APPROPRIATE.
THERE'S NO TIME FOR JOKES, WASP! WE'VE GOT TO... FIND A WAY BACK TO EARTH... AND SWIFTLY!
I -- TRAPPED SOME AIR, BUT THE STRAIN -- INTENSE --
-- COULD EXPAND -- EQUALIZE THE PRESSURE SOMEWHAT -- BUT THEN YOU WOULDN'T BE ABLE TO BREATHE --
ALWAYS TALKIN', BIG BRAIN -- EVEN WHEN EVERYONE ALREADY KNOWS THE JAM WE'RE IN.
IF SUZIE WAS AWAKE, SHE'D JUST POP US ALL INTA ONE'A HER FORCE-FIELDS, AN' WE'D BE FINE --
AND THOR AND I COULD SURVIVE IN SPACE, AND EVEN TOW REED, BUT THERE'S NOWHERE TO TOW HIM TO --
-- AND WE CAN'T GET OUTSIDE WITHOUT KILLING EVERYONE ELSE --
FOR A MOMENT, IRON MAN THINKS THAT THE PROBLEMS THE SURVIVING THUNDERBOLTS FACED SEEM TO HAVE SOLVED THEMSELVES FAIRLY NEATLY --

-- BUT THEN HIS HELMET-RADIO CRACKLES TO LIFE --
AHOY THE AVENGERS! AHOY, AVENGERS AND FANTASTIC FOUR --
-- THIS IS MACH-1, ABOARD THE SPACE STATION SAMAROBRYN.
PREPARE TO BE BROUGHT ABOARD.
THIS IS GREAT, ABE -- BY RIGGING SAMAROBRYN TO COME TO US --
-- YOU NOT ONLY SAVED US --
-- YOU SAVED ALL OF THEM, AS WELL!
YEAH, YEAH, AND I'M STILL NOT SURE THIS IS THE SMARTEST THING WE COULD DO --
-- BUT NO USE CRABBING ABOUT IT NOW...
AND, MINUTES LATER, AFTER ALL ARE SAFELY ABOARD...
SO, HEROES...
...WHAT NOW?
WHADDAYA MEAN, "WHAT NOW?"
YER A BUNCH'A SLIMY SUPER-CREEPS, AN' YER GOIN' TA JAIL! THAT'S WHAT NOW!

THAT MAY BE, Mr. GRIMM -- BUT WE DID SAVE YOUR LIVES -- AND WE DID DESTROY THE THREAT OF ZEMO, AFTER HE'D CAPTURED ALL OF YOU --
-- IRON MAN WILL ATTEST TO THAT.
WELL, YES. I'VE GOT TO ADMIT, THEY --
THEY WERE THE ONES WHO PUT ZEMO IN POWER IN THE FIRST PLACE!
AND LET'S NOT FORGET, THEY DESTROYED AVENGERS MANSION ONCE, AND BEAT JARVIS AND HERCULES NEARLY TO DEATH --
-- AND THAT'S NOT EVEN COUNTING ALL THE PEOPLE WHO'VE DIED OVER THE LAST FEW DAYS!
HEY, IT'S NOT THAT SIMPLE. THEY MAY HAVE STARTED OFF WRONG, BUT THEY DID THE RIGHT THING IN THE END, AND --
HEY, HAVE YOU SEEN FOUR FREEDOMS PLAZA LATELY, PURPLE-PUSS?
WANNA BUNK IN THERE A FEW DAYS, SEE IF YOU STILL FEEL SO FORGIVIN' OF THESE --
THIS ISN'T A DECISION WE HAVE TO MAKE NOW, PEOPLE.
IN FACT, A DECISION WE GET TO MAKE AT ALL. THE THUNDERBOLTS CAN ANSWER TO THE PROPER AUTHORITIES FOR WHAT THEY'VE DONE --
-- AND ALL THE FACTORS CAN BE WEIGHED, GOOD AND BAD.
THAT'S WHAT WE HAVE A JUSTICE SYSTEM FOR, AFTER ALL -- TO MEASURE CULPABILITY, AND DECIDE ON THE APPROPRIATE RESPONSE.
SO, METEORITE, LET ME ASK THE QUESTION OF YOU. WHAT NOW? DO YOU PLAN TO RESIST BEING BROUGHT IN, AND STANDING TRIAL?
Ahh...

NO, CAPTAIN.
WE WON'T RESIST, AND WE APPRECIATE YOUR FAIRNESS.
AND WHETHER METEORITE TRULY MEANS THAT --
-- OR WHETHER SHE'S JUST SAYING WHATEVER WILL GET THEM BACK TO EARTH AND GIVE THEM A CHANCE TO ESCAPE --
-- NO ONE MAY EVER KNOW.
Huh?
WH- WHAT--?
CRIPES! THEY'RE GONE!
I DON'T BELIEVE IT! I JUST DON'T BELIEVE IT! WE HAD THEM -- HAD THEM RIGHT IN FRONT OF US! AND WE JUST LET THEM ESCAPE!
I DUNNO, JAN.
THAT DIDN'T LOOK LIKE ANY ESCAPE TO ME. IN FACT, THEY LOOKED AS SURPRISED AS ANY OF US.
AYE, FRIEND HAWKEYE. BUT THE FACT DOTH REMAIN -- THERE BE NO KNOWING WHERE THE THUNDERBOLTS HATH GONE --
-- OR INDEED, WHETHER THEY E'ER SHALL RETURN --!
IT AIN'T OVER YET!

THE MIGHTY
THOR
GODSTORM

THE MIGHTY THOR IN:
GODSTORM
WILF! HO WILF!
WE NEED YOUR SWORDARM TO REPEL THOSE SNOT-NOSES LED BY GUNNAR'S SON! UP, BOY, UP!
The Coast of the North Sea, in the year 912 A.D....
WOULD THAT I COULD, ULLER--BUT I CANNOT.
I HAVE BEEN TASKED WITH MENDING THESE OLD FISHING NETS--AND I FEAR I CAN MAKE NEITHER HEAD NOR TAIL OF IT.
I CANNOT EVEN UNTANGLE THE CURSED THINGS. I HAVE TRIED FOR HOURS, IT SEEMS--
--AND ALL I END UP WITH IS MORE SNARLS, AND RAW FINGERS!
HA! THEN COME TO WAR, WILF--VENT YOUR IRE ON GUNNAR'S SPAWN!
WHO CARES ABOUT NETS, ANYWAY? FORGET THEM--YOU KNOW THAT OLD NONNA WILL FIX THEM, IN TIME.
GIVING UP IN THE FACE OF ADVERSITY? IS THAT THE MARK OF A VIKING?
1

HUH? Y-YOUR PARDON, ELDER-- I DID NOT SEE YOU THERE.
BUT I MEANT NOTHING--NOTHING BUT TO GIVE WILF HERE A RESPITE FROM DRUDGERY, AND TO EXERCISE HIS SKILLS AT--
SILENCE! YOU ARE A TEMPTER AND A WASTREL-- I SEE IT IN YOUR EYES.
WERE THE FUTURE OF THE NORTHMEN'S RACE ENTRUSTED TO SUCH AS YOU, OUR GLORIES WOULD BE ENDED IN A GENERATION.
YOU SHUN WORK IN FAVOR OF GAMES AND FOOLERY. YOU HAVE NO FIRE, NO HEART. I DESPAIR AT THE SIGHT, AND FEAR FOR THE FUTURE.
TRULY, SIR-- HE MEANT NO HARM. BUT I CONFESS-- I DO NOT UNDER-STAND.
ARE WE NOT WARRIORS? SHOULD WE NOT TEST AND HONE OUR SKILL AT BATTLE, AGAINST OUR FUTURE VOYAGES OF PLUNDER?
PLUNDER? WHAT DO FINGERLINGS LIKE YOURSELVES KNOW OF SUCH THINGS? THERE IS MORE TO THE NORTHMEN THAN MERE PLUNDER!
SHOULD YOU TRULY SEEK THE FIRE OF A WARRIOR'S HEART, THE WAY TO TRIUMPH OVER ALL CHALLENGES--THE SECRET IS THERE, IN FRONT OF YOUR EYES. A SECRET WORTH THE KNOWING.
A PITY THAT THE CALLOW YOUNG ARE SO DEAF TO IT.
UH... SECRET, SIR? I-IF WE COULD BUT HEAR...
PAH. WASTED BREATH, I AM SURE OF IT. STILL, FOLLOW ME.

AND NOW, I SIT UPON THIS ANCIENT STUMP-- ITS ROOTS SINKING DEEP INTO THE EARTH, LIKE YGGDRASIL, THE WORLD TREE, DEEP INTO THE PAST.
SO OPEN YOUR EARS...
...FOR YOUR FIRST STEP ON THE PATHWAY TO MANHOOD.
BUT BE WARNED-- KNOWLEDGE ALONE IS NOT ENOUGH. ONLY THROUGH DEEDS CAN ONE TRULY EARN THE TRUTH I AM ABOUT TO SHOW YOU.
THERE IS ONE AMONG US WHO TRULY KNOWS, WHOSE BLOOD SINGS WITH THE SECRET. DO YOU SEE, AS HE DIRECTS THE LOADING OF THE LONGSHIPS?
HAVE YOU EVER NOTICED SOMETHING PECULIAR IN HIS ATTIRE?
CHIEF HARALD?
DO YOU MEAN...?
THAT PIECE OF STONE HE WEARS ON A THONG? HE IS NEVER WITH-OUT IT.
3

YES, THAT CHIP OF STONE. HAVE YOU NEVER WONDERED WHY HE WEARS IT?
THAT CHIP HAS A STORY, AS ANCIENT AS OUR OWN BEGINNINGS.
AND IT IS THAT TALE I TELL YOU NOW, A TALE OF MEN, GODS AND MORE...
...A TALE KNOWN TO THOSE WHO'VE HEARD IT AS...
The Tale of the Mighty Thor and the Storm that Rebelled
It begins FAR from here, in mighty ASGARD, home to the gods...
...it begins on a day that THOR, God of Thunder, was barely into manhood, as he accompanied FRIGGA and her HANDMAIDENS on a picnic outing...
IT IS MOST KIND OF BALDER AND THEE TO ACT AS OUR HONOR GUARD, THOR. IT HATH BEEN LONG INDEED SINCE WE ENJOYED SUCH A DIVERSION.
'TIS NOTHING, MILADY-- THE HONOR IS ALL OURS. AND THOU COULDST NOT HAVE ASKED FOR A FINER DAY...
PERHAPS NOT, YOUNG THOR. SEE, FROM THE EAST-- STORM CLOUDS BEGIN TO ROLL IN...

THESE CLOUDS-- THEY LOOM MOST OMINOUSLY, AS IF SWOLLEN WITH EVIL! BUT HOW COULD THEY HAVE APPEARED SO SWIFTLY?
In truth, it was LOKI, god of michief and evil-- JEALOUS at not being chosen by Frigga, he had cast a spell to ruin the day...
FEAR NOT, MILADY.
IT IS ONLY RECENTLY THAT I HAVE WON STEWARDSHIP OF MY HAMMER MJOLNIR-- AND WITH IT, MY FULL POWER OVER THE STORMS.
BUT FOR ALL THAT I BE NEW TO IT, STILL AM I THE GOD OF THUNDER! STILL AM I MASTER OF THE LIGHTNING!
AND THE GOD OF THUNDER SPEAKS!
SHRINK, CLOUDS, BY THE COMMAND OF THOR! SHRINK AND DWINDLE--
--UNTIL THY MALIGN POWER IS REDUCED TO NAUGHT!
AND NOW BEGONE--
--AND TROUBLE US NO MORE!
5

ZOUNDS! YON CLOUDS DRIFT AWAY... HARMLESS!
THOR, SON OF MY HEART--WE ARE ALL IN THY DEBT! CLEAR SKIES LIE AHEAD!
AND YET, BEHOLD--THE TINY CLOUD SEEMS NOT TO HAVE LOST ALL ITS FURY!
IT LOOSES A SMALL DOWNPOUR--A BRIEF SHOWER--ON SOME POOR, UNLUCKY SOUL. BUT WHO--?

HA HA HA HA HA! THE POOR SOUL IS LOKI HIMSELF! WHAT TERRIBLE LUCK TO BEFALL A GOD AS PRIDEFUL AS HE!
STILL, MISTRESS--HE IS SAID TO BE GOD OF MISCHIEF, AFTER ALL.
SURELY HE CAN SEE THE HUMOR IN THIS...

A THOUSAND PARDONS, HALF-BROTHER! MY SKILL IS NOT YET WHAT IT MUST BE--I SHALL HAVE TO PRACTICE MORE!
BUT STILL, 'TIS ONLY WATER--NO HARM HATH BEEN DONE, EH?

It was actually the power of Loki's SPELL that drew the waning storm to him. But for all that Thor's apologies fell on DEAF EARS...
BY ALL THE SPIRIT OF NIFLHEIM! TRULY, THOR--THO SHALT PAY FOR TH HUMILIATION-

Wasting no time, the evil-hearted young Asgardian set out on a JOURNEY...
...a journey to CRAGMOUTH itself, the FORBIDDEN DWELLING of the storms, when they do not RAGE in our skies!
THERE! THERE SHALL I FIND MY REVENGE!
Even the gods themselves SHUNNED the dread labyrinths within. But Loki did not HESITATE. He entered, driven by RAGE...
...and soon, he began to hear the WHISPERING of foreboding WINDS...
GO BACK, PUNY ASGARDIAN!
THIS IS NOT A PLACE FOR YOUR KIND! GO BACK--OR FEAR DEATH--!
But Loki STRODE ON...
I HAVE IMPORTANT BUSINESS--BUT NOT WITH MERE WINDS! I SEEK THE MOST POWERFUL OF ALL STORMS!
THEN YOU HAVE FOUND HIM, GODLING! NOW SPEAK, QUICKLY--
--ERE I DECIDE TO HURL THEE INTO THE DEPTHS, NEVER TO ARISE!
COME TO SPEAK TO THEE OF INJUSTICE, GREAT ONE! TO SPEAK TO THEE... OF THOR!
THOR? HE IS OUR PATRON, GODLING. ALL WHO SERVE HIM HERE DO SO WITH GREAT PRIDE...
BUT THAT PRIDE IS NOT SHOWN IN RETURN, GREAT ONE. THOR CARES NOTHING FOR THEE--TO HIM, THOU ART BUT A SLAVE...
The storm darkened with anger and FLASHED with lightning. But Loki spoke on, dripping HONEYED, POISONOUS WORDS into its hearing...
AND NO MAN ALIVE KNOWS WHAT LOKI SAID. BUT LOKI IS CUNNING, AND HE SPOKE FOR A LONG, LONG TIME...
7

AND THE RESULT OF LOKI'S MACHINATIONS WOULD BE KNOWN SOON... BUT NOT IN ASGARD. FOR LESS THAN A MOONCHANGE LATER, ON THESE VERY WATERS...
...A DARK AND DANGEROUS FLEET SAILED FOR OUR SHORES.
THIS WAS LONG BEFORE THE TIME OF ANY MAN ALIVE TODAY, BUT STILL DID OUR CLANS FARM THESE LANDS AND FISH THESE WATERS.
AND OUR CHIEFTAIN DID ORDER OUT THE FLEET, TO MEET THE FOE...
BERZERKIR, OUT OF THULE. THEY SEEK NOT PLUNDER, BUT BLOOD, AND DEATH...
THEY OUTNUMBER US, MY CHIEFTAIN. AND IT IS SAID THAT THE BERSERKIR KNOW NO MERCY, THAT THEY FIGHT 'TIL THEY DIE, OR 'TIL THE LAST FOE FALLS.
THIS SHALL BE A BLOODY DAY INDEED.
LET THEM DO THEIR WORST, RANULF. WE SHALL DO OUR BEST.
I PRAY OUR GODS HEAR OUR PLEAS, FOR ONLY WITH THEIR HELP--
WE ARE VIKINGS, RANULF. WE DO NOT PLEAD.
HEAR ME, GODS OF FAR ASGARD! HEAR ME, THOR! HEAR ME, TYR AND HEIMDALL! WE CALL ON YOU, NOT FOR AID, FOR OUR STRENGTH IS OUR OWN
WE CALL ON YOU MERELY TO TAKE NOTICE--TO SEE THAT WE ARE NORTHMEN, WORTHY OF YOU! SEE HOW WE FIGHT, THOR! SEE HOW WE DIE!

And high above, Thor HEARD. And Thor came, as requested, to see how our brave men faced ADVERSITY.
And Thor was most DEEPLY impressed...
SUCH COURAGE AS THIS IS RARE INDEED-- AND SHOULD NOT PERISH FROM THE FACE OF MIDGARD.
THOUGH THESE MEN DID NOT ASK THOR'S AID, AS BEFITS THEIR WARRIOR CODE--
--STILL, THEY SHALL HAVE IT, AS BEFITS THE CHOICE OF A GOD!
BLOW, WINDS! CRACK, SKIES! I CALL UPON THEE, STORM OF THE AIR!
I CALL UPON THE MIGHTIEST OF THY NUMBER! COME HITHER, GREATEST OF STORMS --COME HITHER AND APPEAR--
--NOW!
BAMM!
And...
THOU ART HERE!
COME, THEN--RAGE OVER THE SEA! RAGE LOW-- AND STRIKE THAT INVADING FLEET, BLOWING THEM AWAY--SO FAR THEY WILL NEVER FIND THEIR WAY HERE AGAIN!
9

And even as Thor gave his COMMANDS, in Loki's private chambers in Asgard...
THE FOOL! THIS IS MY CHANCE!
THOR SEEKS TO AID THOSE PATHETIC MORTALS--AND THUS DELIVERS TO ME THE OPPORTUNITY I HAVE BEEN WAITING FOR!
HEAR ME, O STORM! HEAR THE WORDS OF LOKI, WHO CAME TO THEE AS A FRIEND!
IT IS AS I TOLD THEE!
THOR MERELY USES THEE, TO SATISFY HIS CASUAL WHIMS! PUTS THEE AT THE SERVICE OF MERE MORTALS, WHO SHOULD BE BENEATH THY NOTICE!
SUCH A TASK OFFENDS THY DIGNITY--IS AN AFFRONT TO THY MIGHT! THOU ART TOO GREAT FOR SUCH AS THIS!
And the storm hovered, FROZEN, unsure what to do...
WHAT CHICANERY IS THIS? THE STORM DOES NOT STRIKE--DOES NOT SMITE THE ENEMY!
HO, WINDS--ATTEND THY MASTER! THOR HATH ORDERED THEE--AND THOU MUST OBEY!
Loki arrived, then, INVISIBLE to all but the storm itself...
I CALL ON THEE, STORM--!
DOST THOU HEAR? HE ORDERS THEE LIKE A DOG!
SURELY THOU UNDERSTANDEST NOW! THOU CANNOT FOLLOW A BUFFOON SUCH AS THIS! THINE IS THE POWER! THINE IS THE MIGHT!
THOU MUST TAKE THY POWER UNTO THYSELF, GREAT ONE--

--AND DESTROY THY SLAVE-MASTER!
DESTROY THOR!!
YES!
NO LONGER SHALL I OBEY! NOW SHALL I BE FREE! NOW SHALL THOR DIE!
And the storm TURNED on Thor, striking him with UNIMAGINABLE WINDS, tearing him into the SKIES.
And below...
MY CHIEFTAIN! WE MUST MAKE FOR LAND! WE CANNOT WITH-STAND THESE--
NO! IF I TRULY SEE WHAT I THINK I DO--WE MUST PUSH FORWARD! INTO THE STORM!
MAN THE OARS, MEN! FORWARD! PRESS FORWARD!
AIEEEE!
As they did, the ship was BATTERED, shaken like a child's toy, but still he pressed on...
SIR! WE'LL LOSE THE SHIP!
ONWARD! ROW ONWARD!
Above...
MY HAMMER!
THE MAELSTROM WRENCHED MJOLNIR FROM MY GRASP--AND I CANNOT BREATHE, CANNOT CONCENTRATE--
--CANNOT CALL IT TO RETURN TO ME WITH ENOUGH WILL--!
And Thor's breath grew SHALLOW, and his vision began to darken...
11

HA HA HA HA HA HA
HA
THAT-- THAT FACE!
AM I IMAGINING THINGS, OR--?!
And surely, it would have been the END of Thor, but...
A SHIP! A SHIP, BRAVING EVEN THIS UNCON-TROLLED FURY!
THEN--THEN THOR HATH A CHANCE--
--AND HE SHALL SEIZE IT!
WOM
NO, THOR! NO! THOU WILT DIE!
THOU WILT DIE--AND I SHALL BE MASTER!
SO--IT IS THE STORM ITSELF I FACE, EH?
INSOLENT BRAGGART! THOU SHALT NOT PREVAIL!
THOUGH THOU STRIKEST MJOLNIR WITH BOLT UPON BOLT OF LIGHTNING IN AN EFFORT TO DESTROY IT, THY MOMENT HATH PASSED!
THOR HATH A PLACE TO STAND NOW--AND HE WILL NOT BE DENIED! BY THE POWER OF ALL-FATHER ODIN, THE HAMMER MJOLNIR IS MINE--
--AND I DO CALL IT TO RETURN TO MY HAND! COME TO ME, MJOLNIR--
--AND LET THE POWER OF THIS STORM BE BROKEN!

And in the sudden calm that FOLLOWED...
DO--DO MY EYES DECEIVE ME?!
IT IS THOR HIMSELF-- THE GOD OF THUNDER!
THOR-- ON OUR SHIP!
HAIL TO THEE, MIGHTY ONE. WE OWE YOU OUR VERY LIVES!
NOT SO, BRAVE VIKING. 'TIS I WHO OWE THEE.
THOU COULDST HAVE SAVED THYSELVES, OUTRUN THE STORM--BUT THOU KNEW NOT FEAR, AND CAME TO MY AID WITHOUT FLAGGING!
THE BERZERKIR!
THE WINDS GONE, THEY COME ONWARD STILL! GREAT THOR, COULD YOU PERHAPS--?
RANULF!
WE DO NOT ASK AID, RANULF! WE ARE VIKINGS, AND WE FIGHT OUR OWN BATTLES. GIRD YOURSELVES, MEN--
--FOR THE BATTLE IS NIGH!
THOU DOST NOT ASK MY AID, PROUD CHIEFTAIN--BUT THOU HAST EARNED IT NONETHELESS. AND IN ANY CASE--
--THOR HATH ANOTHER DEBT TO PAY THIS DAY!
HO, MIGHTIEST OF STORMS! THOR DOTH CALL ON THEE AGAIN, WHERE THOU LINGER IN THE AIR!
AND SUCH IS THOR'S RAGE-- AND THOR'S UNFETTERED POWER--
--THAT HE WILL NOT BE DENIED!
NO! I WILL DENY THEE!
13

I AM THE POWER! I AM THE GODSTORM!
I WILL KILL THEE-- KILL THEE--!
But such was the power of Thor's command that the godstorm BUCKLED before it--buckled and FELL--
SIRE! THE VIKINGS EMPLOY SORCERY!
ON, YOU FOOLS! ROW ON! THEY STAND AGAINST US--AND THEY MUST FALL!
SIRE! BEFORE US-- THE WATER BEGINS TO SWIRL--TO OPEN A GREAT CHASM--
NO!
NO!
I CANNOT BE DENIED IN THIS! I CANNOT--!
But...
THOU WILT NOT ENDANGER ANY AGAIN, REBELLIOUS ONE! DOWN THOU GOEST, TO THE SEAFLOOR, AND BELOW--DOWN TO THE ROCK OF THE EARTH--
--WHERE THOU WILT BE TRAPPED--FOREVER!
NO! I WILL ESCAPE! I WILL RETURN!
I WILL RETURN ONE DAY--AND I WILL HAVE MY REVENGE--!
IT IS DONE. THE SO-CALLED GODSTORM IS PUNISHED--AND THE BERZERKIR FLEET BROKEN.
THE WATERS OF THE NORTH SEA WILL COO THEIR ARDOR--AND THEY WILL LIM HOME, AND LICK THEIR WOUNDS.
OUR ETERNAL THANKS, GREAT ONE.

Soon, in our VILLAGE, which was young in those days...
HO! NORTHMEN AND WOMEN! GATHER ROUND, FOR THOR, GOD OF THUNDER, HATH SOMETHING TO SAY TO THEE!
THOU SHOULD HAVE GREAT PRIDE IN THY CHIEFTAIN -- FOR TRULY, HE HAS A WARRIOR'S HEART, A VIKING'S FIRE!
FACED WITH DANGER, HE MET IT! HE DID NOT SHRINK, HE DID NOT QUAIL. AND FACED WITH THE SIGHT OF ANOTHER IN PERIL --
-- HE BRAVED GREATER DANGER STILL, TO AID ME. HE UNFLINCHINGLY SET TO HIS TASKS, WITHOUT THOUGHT OF FAILURE OR OF SURRENDER.
LEARN FROM HIM, AS THOU DOST REPAIR THY SHIPS, AND LIVE THY LIVES, LEARN THE VALUE OF DETERMINATION, OF STEADFASTNESS. FOR IT IS A TRAIT THAT SHALL SERVE THEE WELL INDEED.
AND HO -- 'TWOULD SEEM THAT THY SHIPS WERE NOT THE ONLY THINGS DAMAGED.
MY OWN HAMMER WAS CRACKED -- CHIPPED BY THE FURIOUS BARRAGE OF LIGHTNING IT ENDURED.
BUT NO MATTER -- IT TOO CAN BE REPAIRED. AND AS A REWARD FOR THY BRAVERY, GOOD CHIEFTAIN, I PRESENT YOU WITH A GIFT --
-- SOMETHING THAT DOUBTLESS NO MORTAL WILL E'ER RECEIVE AGAIN.
NOW FARE THEE WELL, ALL!
AND KNOW, BRAVE ONE, THAT THOU HAST THE GRATITUDE OF THOR! AND SHOULD THOU -- OR THY FAMILY -- EVER NEED MY AID --
-- I SHALL BE THERE!
15

THAT--THAT HAPPENED HERE?! AND CHIEF HARALD--HE IS DESCENDED FROM THAT LONG-AGO CHIEFTAIN--
--AND HE WEARS A PIECE OF THOR'S HAMMER?!
YES, BUT--
AND THAT STORM--IT IS OUT THERE? UNDER THE SEAFLOOR RIGHT OFF OUR COAST? IS IT STILL THERE? DID IT EVER ESCAPE?
WILL IT?
HMM. I HAD INTENDED MY TALE TO ILLUSTRATE THE VALUE OF PERSER-VERANCE IN THE FACE OF ADVERSITY--
--BUT IT SEEMS I HAVE AWOKEN MORE CURIOSITY THAN UNDER-STANDING.
STILL, YOU ASK TELLING QUESTIONS, DARK-HAIRED ONE. NO, THE GODSTORM HAS NOT ESCAPED--NOT YET.
AS TO THE FUTURE--
--WELL, WE MIGHT BE ABLE TO DISCOVER SOMETHING ABOUT THAT. WORTH A TRY, AT LEAST, HM?
SPIRIT OF DISCOVERY, EH?
I TAKE THE RUNESTICKS--
--THE BONES OF THE WORLD--AND I ASK THE FATES--ASK THEM FOR SIGHT--!

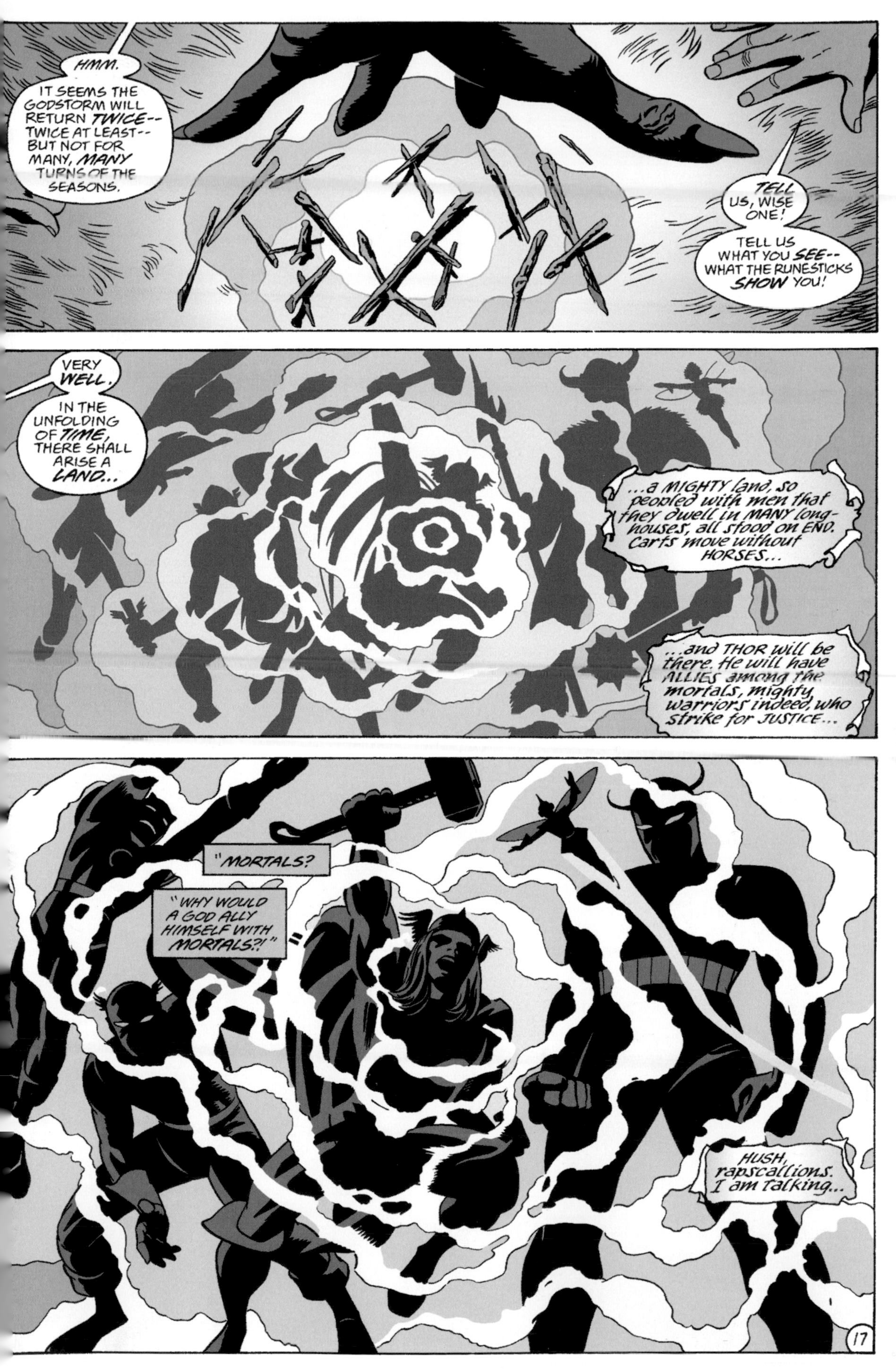
HMM.
IT SEEMS THE GODSTORM WILL RETURN TWICE-- TWICE AT LEAST-- BUT NOT FOR MANY, MANY TURNS OF THE SEASONS.
TELL US, WISE ONE!
TELL US WHAT YOU SEE-- WHAT THE RUNESTICKS SHOW YOU!
VERY WELL.
IN THE UNFOLDING OF TIME, THERE SHALL ARISE A LAND...
...a MIGHTY land, so peopled with men that they dwell in MANY long-houses, all stood on END. Carts move without HORSES...
...and THOR will be there. He will have ALLIES among the mortals, mighty warriors indeed, who strike for JUSTICE...
"MORTALS?
"WHY WOULD A GOD ALLY HIMSELF WITH MORTALS?!"
HUSH, rapscallions. I am talking...
17

THE WHEEL OF TIME TURNS, BUT THE NATURE OF MAN DOES NOT. STILL THERE ARE SCOUNDRELS, AND STILL THERE ARE CHAMPIONS--AND STILL THE INNOCENT ARE CAUGHT BETWEEN.
SO IT IS IN THE EVENTS I AM ABOUT TO DESCRIBE, IN A STORY WE MIGHT CALL...
The Tale of the Mighty Thor and the Man Who Made Weather!
LOOKS LIKE THAT "WEATHER-MAKER" LOUSE IS TRAPPED, CAP--HE'S GOT NOWHERE TO RETREAT TO.
I AGREE, HIGHPOCKETS--BUT I'M SUSPICIOUS. THERE'S TOO MUCH HERE WE DON'T UNDERSTAND. LIKE WHO HE IS--AND WHY HE'S DOING THIS!
PLEASE, EVERYONE--STAY BACK! LET US HANDLE THIS!
C'MON, GIANT-MAN--QUIT BLOCKIN' THE VIEW!
GIVE BUT THE WORD, CAPTAIN AMERICA--AND THOR'S HAMMER SHALL STRIKE!
STRIKE AWAY, HANDSOME!
BUT LEAVE SOMETHING FOR THE WINSOME WASP TO CLEAN UP!
ARE WE PLANNING TO TALK HIM INTO UNCONSCIOUSNESS, AVENGERS--OR ARE WE READY TO TAKE HIM?
AW, WE GOT AS MUCH RIGHT TO SEE THE SHOW AS ANYONE!

READY? YOU CAN NEVER BE READY FOR THE WEATHER-MAKER!
UHHHH!
CARSTAIRS-- YOU'RE HURTING ME--!
SHOOSH
SHOOSH
COWER, AVENGERS! COWER BEFORE MY UNPARALLELED METEOROLOGICAL GENIUS! FOR WHAT OTHER MAN CAN COMMAND THE ELEMENTS AS I DO?
WHAT OTHER MAN CAN BARRAGE YOU WITH A DEADLY SHOWER OF HAIL?!
SORRY, PAL-- BUT COWERING'S NOT IN OUR CONTRACT!
HAIL--'GAINST THE GOD OF THUNDER? THIS VILLAIN KNOWS NOT WHAT HE FACES!
YOU SAID IT, GOLDILOCKS! ONE WELL-PLACED WASP'S STING-- AND HE'LL BE BEGGING FOR A NICE, COZY JAIL CELL!
THERE! ONE SWEEP OF MY MYSTIC MALLET-- AND HIS HEINOUS ATTACK IS SCATTERED TO THE FOUR WINDS!
BUT HOLD! IRON MAN HATH BEEN STRUCK-- CAUGHT IN A STREAM OF FREEZING RAIN!
NICE GOING, WASP! YOU DREW HIS ATTENTION--
--AND NOW I'VE GOT HIM IMMOBILIZED!
AND NOW FOR THE COUP DE GRACE-- ONE STING, COMING RIGHT UP!
DON'T--DON'T WORRY ABOUT ME, THOR! ARMOR JOINTS--FROZEN! BUT I CAN TAKE THE FALL!
JUST CLEAR THE STREET--AND GIVE ME ANOTHER CRACK AT THIS JOKER WHEN I'M OUT OF THIS!
19

YOUR STING--HAH! IT CAN'T PENETRATE MY BODY ARMOR!
BUT AS LONG AS YOU'VE SWOOPED SO CLOSE, FEEL MY STING--
--THE STING OF HURRICANE-FORCE WINDS!
CLIK
CARSTAIRS... DON'T!
WHOA! I MAY NOT BE MISTER FANTASTIC, HONEY--BUT WITH THESE ARMS, I CAN MUSTER A BOARDING-HOUSE REACH WITH THE BEST OF 'EM!
GOT YOU!
TH-THANKS, DARLING! WIND--KNOCKED THE BREATH OUT OF ME! BUT I'M NO HELPLESS SIDEKICK--I'LL BE FINE!
JUST--SAVE THAT GIRL!
And those "Avengers" pressed on, intent on just that...
UHH!
NO!
THIS MALEFACTOR'S WEAPONRY IS IMPRESSIVE INDEED--TO HOLD BACK THE MIGHTY AVENGERS LIKE THIS!
BUT HE SHALL NOT STAND--NOT WHILE THE POWER OF THOR STANDS AGAINST HIM!
But even as Thor prepared to UNLEASH Mjolnir...
THOR--ATTEND ME! THY FATHER HATH NEED OF THEE--IMMEDIATELY!
ALL-FATHER ODIN! BUT WHAT--?
2

THE TROLLS HAVE CHALLENGED ASGARD'S RIGHT OF PASSAGE THROUGH THE NINE WORLDS! THEY ASSEMBLE OUTSIDE THE GATES FOR A WAR-PARLEY--
--AND WE MUST MEET THEM IN STRENGTH! AS PRINCE OF THE REALM, THY PRESENCE IS REQUIRED--WITHOUT DELAY!
FATHER, MY LOVE FOR THEE AND RESPECT FOR MY DUTY KNOWS NO BOUNDS--BUT I AM ENGAGED IN COMBAT, EVEN AS WE SPEAK! THE TROLLS MAY BE GATHERING--BUT THERE IS DANGER ON MIDGARD NOW!
I SHALL DO MY BEST TO END THINGS SWIFTLY--AND WILL JOIN THEE IN ASGARD AS SOON AS I AM ABLE!
THOU DEFIEST THY FATHER? DEFIEST HIS ROYAL ORDER?
HEAR THIS, MY SON--YOU SHALL RETURN TO ASGARD, AND SHALL RETURN BY SUNDOWN! I WILL BROOK NO EXCUSES!
And in a thunderclap heard only by the thunder god--Odin VANISHED!
While, ATOP the great structure...
STOP STRUGGLING, MAUREEN--YOU'LL ONLY MAKE THINGS WORSE!
YOU CANNOT ESCAPE ME. AND YOU KNOW--YOU KNOW YOU ARE THE REASON I DO THIS...
YOU'RE HATEFUL, CARSTAIRS! HATEFUL! I'LL NEVER FORGIVE YOU--AND I HOPE THEY LOCK YOU UP AND THROW AWAY THE KEY!
YOU'LL CHANGE YOUR TUNE, MAUREEN, I'M--EH?!
WHO DARES--?!
THE NAME'S CAPTAIN AMERICA, FRIEND. MAYBE YOU'VE HEARD OF ME.
YOU LET DOWN YOUR GUARD FOR AN INSTANT--BUT THAT WAS ALL I NEEDED!
21

BAH! I'M PREPARED FOR ANY CONTINGENCY! MY POWER-PACK DOESN'T JUST FUEL MY WEAPONS -- IT LETS ME FLY, AS WELL!
JUST A FEW MORE SECONDS -- OF THERMAL WAVES --
ZZZZMMMM
DON'T CROW TOO LOUD, BUSTER! DON'T FORGET, THE AVENGERS ARE TEAM PLAYERS --
-- OR DO YOU NEED A REMINDER?
GIANT-MAN! I THOUGHT YOU'D BE A FROZEN CORPSE BY NOW!
KRAKK
NOPE -- JUST PORSICLE TEMPERATURE!
AND ALL WARM AND TOASTY NOW -- THANKS TO IRON MAN!
BUT THIS POP-GUN OF YOURS IS GETTING TO BE A NUISANCE -- SO LET'S JUST DIVEST YOU OF IT!
YOU THINK MY WEATHER-CANNON IS MY ENTIRE ARSENAL?
A FEW FRIGI-CUSSION GRENADES SHOULD DISABUSE YOU OF THAT NOTION!
HAH!
AND NOW...
POOM!
UNH!
NNH!

REMEMBER WHAT I SAID ABOUT TEAMWORK, WEATHER-MAKER? WHILE THE OTHERS KEPT YOU BUSY--I FREED YOUR HOSTAGE!
UNHAND HER, CAPTAIN AMERICA-- AND RETURN HER TO ME--
--OR YOU'LL DIE WHERE YOU STAND!
MISTER, NOBODY THREATENS AN AVENGER--LEAST OF ALL A TIN-PLATED TINHORN WITH DELUSIONS OF GRANDEUR!
ZZZWHPPP
YOUR ARMOR SEEMS TOUGH ENOUGH TO SPARE YOU INJURY--
--BUT MY SHIELD OUGHT TO BE ENOUGH TO CRACK YOU LIKE A LOBSTER!
PERHAPS, CAPTAIN-- WERE IT TO STRIKE ME!
SSSSSS
SSSSS
YOU ARE QUITE SKILLED WITH YOUR SHIELD, HERO--BUT ALL WEAPONS CAN BE TURNED AGAINST THEIR WIELDER BY THE RIGHT POWER!
THE POWER FOR INSTANCE--
--OF 200 M.P.H. HOT MISTS!
KRAKH
THE WALL!
GET DOWN, MISS-- BEFORE IT--!
23

NO! NO!
AIEEEEEE
CAP, AND THE GIRL-- THEY'VE BOTH BEEN BURIED IN THE RUBBLE!
WAIT! THOR'S ON THE SCENE! AND CAP LOOKS OKAY, BUT THE GIRL--!
MY PARDON, AVENGERS, FOR ALLOWING MYSELF TO BE DISTRACTED DURING THE BATTLE. DEMOLISHING HIS POWER-PACK ENDED HIS THREAT.
BUT THE WOMAN IS INJURED-- GRAVELY!
AT LEAST YOU CAUGHT THE WEATHER-MAKER, THOR. I'D LIKE TO SEND HIM TO SING-SING WITH MY SUNDAY PUNCH!
GET IN LINE, BIG MAN!
I-I NEVER MEANT FOR HER TO BE HURT! NEVER!
SHOULD'VE THOUGHT OF THAT A WHILE AGO, CHARLIE...
I'VE RADIOED FOR AN AMBULANCE-- BUT THE FIGHT'S CAUSED SO MUCH TRAFFIC CONGESTION, IT MAY NOT BE ABLE TO GET HERE RIGHT AWAY...
AND BY THE TIME IT DOES, HER WOUNDS MAY PROVE TOO GRIEVOUS TO ADDRESS. HER FATE REMAINS IN OUR HANDS!
LET'S GET HER TO A DOCTOR, THEN-- WHILE I PULL THIS TIGER'S TEETH.
FUNNY HOW HARMLESS HE LOOKS NOW-- LIKE ANY AVERAGE JOE...
JERK!

It would be SUNDOWN soon, and the thunder god KNEW it. But he felt the young woman's FAINT, RAGGED BREATH against his chest-- and knew he could not merely turn her over to OTHERS and depart...
I--I MUST--
--I CAN'T.
NO!
I SHALL SEE TO HER TREATMENT, AVENGERS! DO NOT FEAR-- SHE WILL GET THE BEST MEDICAL ATTENTION--THE BEST! WHATE'ER THE COST!
HUH? WHAT--WHAT WAS THAT ALL ABOUT?
Soon, in the chambers of a local HEALER...
JANE FOSTER!
PREPARE FOR AN OPERATION-- THIS YOUNG WOMAN WILL NOT SURVIVE WITHOUT SPEEDY MINISTRATIONS!
THOR!
Y-YES, OF COURSE--I'LL GET RIGHT ON IT! BUT DR. BLAKE-- HE ISN'T HERE RIGHT NOW--!
HE WILL BE.
JUST SEE TO THE PREPARATIONS, NURSE FOSTER.
And sure enough, once the HELP-MAID was gone...
...Thor knelt, and with the merest TAP of Mjolnir 'gainst the floor...
...he was TRANS-FORMED!
ALL RIGHT, GIRL-- THOR'S DONE HIS BEST. NOW LET'S SEE WHAT I CAN DO FOR YOU...
25

WHA-A-A-A-AT?!
THOR-- TRANSFORMING INTO A *MORTAL*?
THE WOMAN--THE *HELP-MAID*--SHE *KNEW* HIS HUMAN FORM! BUT WHY WOULD HE *DO* SUCH A THING?
HOW WOULD HE COME TO HAVE A *MORT*
LIFE AT ALL?
I CONFESS... I DO NOT *KNOW*.

BUT PERHAPS THE *RUNESTICKS* WILL GRACE US WITH AN ANSWER ONCE AGAIN.
RATTLE RATTLE RATTLE

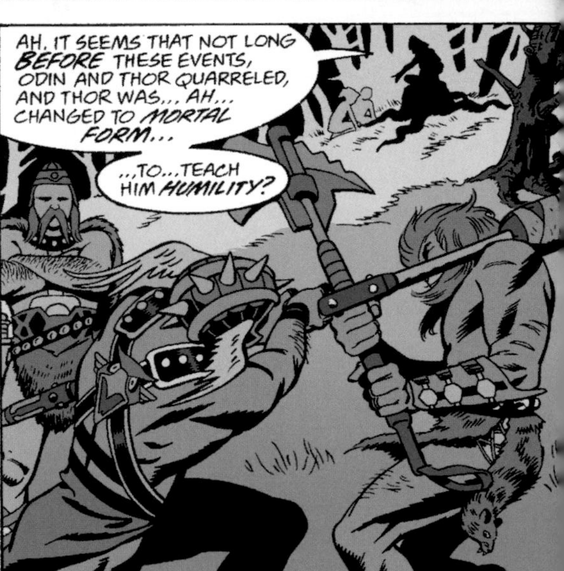
AH. IT SEEMS THAT NOT LONG *BEFORE* THESE EVENTS, ODIN AND THOR QUARRELED, AND THOR WAS... AH... CHANGED TO *MORTAL FORM*...
...TO...TEACH HIM *HUMILITY*?

BUT--THAT'S *MADNESS*! THOR IS A *GOD*! WHAT NEED DOES HE HAVE FOR *HUMILITY*?

AND WHY A *HEALER*? SURELY, EVEN IF THOR WAS MORTAL, HE WOULD BE A *WARRIOR*!

SO, DO I TAKE IT FROM YOUR INTERRUPTIONS THAT YOU DO NOT WANT ME TO *CONTINUE* WITH THIS TALE?
OH, NO-- *NO*! PLEASE-- *CONTINUE*!

VERY WELL. *SILENCE*, THEN.
AND LO--THE NEXT PIECE OF OUR STORY IS *REVEALED* TO US...

In the halls of MIGHTY ASGARD, Odin waited... and WAITED. And as time grew long, he grew more WRATHFUL...
SHADOWS LENGTHEN, AND NIGHT FALLS. AND STILL-- STILL, THOR DOTH NOT RETURN.
I HAVE BEEN PATIENT. MOST PATIENT...
..BUT E'EN MY PATIENCE IS NOT LIMITLESS! WHERE IS HE? WHERE IS THOR?
WHERE IS MY SON?!
THOU DIDST CALL, FATHER?
OH--I SEE IT IS THINE OTHER SON THOU DOST SEEK.
I AM SORRY TO SAY, SIRE, THAT SUNDOWN HAS COME--BOTH HERE AND ON THAT PORTION OF MIDGARD HE FAVORS.
THERE CAN BE BUT ONE CONCLUSION. HE HATH DEFIED THEE-- DEFIED THE ALL-FATHER, THE ALL-POWER--
--PREFERRING TO GAMBOL AND FRITTER AWAY HIS TIME WITH MERE MORTALS.
PERHAPS--PERHAPS SOMETHING PREVENTS HIM FROM RETURNING. I SHALL LOOK ON HIM AND SEE...
And, on Midgard...
IT'S DONE.
THE GIRL WILL LIVE!
27

FORTUNATELY, HER INJURIES, WHILE TELLING, WERE NOT EXTENSIVE. SHE'LL RECOVER QUICKLY, WITH REST.
SHE WAS LUCKY TO HAVE ESCAPED WITHOUT GREATER HARM.
YOU MEAN SHE WAS LUCKY TO HAVE YOU TO HELP HER, DR. BLAKE. I SAW THAT PROCEDURE--
--AND THERE ISN'T ANOTHER DOCTOR ALIVE WHO COULD HAVE SAVED HER.
THAT-- DOESN'T MATTER, JANE. ONLY THE RESULT MATTERS.
FOSTER
ER, DO WE KNOW WHO SHE IS?
NOT REALLY-- SHE WAS MIXED UP WITH THAT WEATHER-MAKER FELLOW ON THE NEWS--
--AND SHE DIDN'T HAVE THE MOST ORTHODOX CHECK-IN.
YOU CAN GET HER PARTICULARS WHEN SHE WAKES UP, HM?
OF COURSE. BUT FOR NOW--YOU'RE TIRED, DOCTOR, AND YOU'VE BEEN WORKING HARD. YOU NEED TO RELAX.
HAVE YOU EATEN? WE COULD GO OUT FOR A LATE DINNER..?
THAT'S KIND OF YOU, JANE.
BUT AFTER SUCH A LONG DAY, I THINK I'LL JUST GO UP TO THE ROOF FOR A FEW MINUTES-- GET SOME FRESH AIR.
MAYBE ANOTHER TIME.
OH, AND I'LL NEED SOME NEW REPORT FORMS SOON--I'M RUNNING LOW. COULD YOU TAKE CARE OF THAT?
THANKS, JANE.
IT'S HOPELESS-- UTTERLY HOPELESS!
I'M NOTHING TO HIM! NOTHING... BUT A NURSE...!

Meantime, HIGH ABOVE, under the night sky...
I'D BETTER CHANGE-- GET TO ASGARD BEFORE THINGS GET ANY WORSE. BUT-- I'VE GOT TO MAKE SURE WHAT HAPPENED TODAY DOESN'T HAPPEN AGAIN.
I ALLOWED MYSELF TO BE DISTRACTED--AND IT WAS SHE WHO ALMOST PAID THE PRICE.
The mortal healer SIGHED--and raised his staff. But then--
I WAS NEEDED, FATHER--NEEDED HERE! I AM SWORN TO PROTECT HUMANITY--AND A LIFE WAS IN DANGER, THROUGH MY INACTION!
I HAD TO STAY, UNTIL--
THY DUTY IS TO THY FATHER, UNRULY ONE! AND IN THIS, THOU HAST FAILED MOST GRIEVOUSLY! BUT NEVER MORE!
--AND MAKE THEE THY TRUE SELF ONCE MORE!
THY TRUE SELF! THOU WOULDST DO WELL TO REMEMBER THAT--

THOU HAST DISOBEYED THY FATHER, THOR! DISOBEYED THY SWORN LIEGE LORD!
EXPLAIN THYSELF!

ZOOF!
I STRIP FROM THEE THY MORTAL GUISE--

--FOR I RETURN THEE NOW TO ASGARD'S GLEAMING HALLS, AND THOU SHALL SEE MIDGARD--
--NEVER AGAIN!
29

And, in the DUNGEONS used in this time to hold prisoners awaiting JUDGMENT...
HEY, WEATHER-BOY-- HOW 'BOUT MAKIN' IT RAIN FOR ME ON SUNDAY? I PROMISED THE OLD LADY I'D TAKE HER TO THE FLOWER SHOW--
--BUT I REALLY DON'T WANT TO, KNOW WHAT I MEAN?
HEY, WHATSAMATTER? NOT SUCH A BIG SHOT WITHOUT YOUR DOO-DADS AND GIZMOS, HUH?
LEAVE ME, YOU IMBECILE. CONFINEMENT IS BAD ENOUGH, WITHOUT HAVING TO ENDURE YOUR HUMOR AS WELL!
GOOD. HE'S GONE!
THE FOOLS--TO THINK I WOULDN'T HAVE A CONTINGENCY PLAN FOR THIS VERY SITUATION!
THIS--MNH! FALSE TOOTH, JAMMED WITH CIRCUITRY, IS ALL I NEED! I NEVER HAD THE CHANCE TO TEST IT--
--BUT IT SHOULD CALL A STORM TO ME, TO FREE ME.
AND I'LL NEED A POWERFUL STORM INDEED TO SHATTER THESE WALLS!
SO REACH OUT, MY LITTLE TECHNOLOGICAL WONDER! REACH OUT--AROUND THE WORLD--AND FIND THE MOST VIOLENT STORM YOU CAN!
REACH OUT, AND--
--AH! GOT SOME-THING! BUT--
CITY DETENTION FACILITY
WHAT--?
MY MIND--FLOODING WITH DARKNESS! WHAT--
--WHAT HAVE I CONTACTED?
YOU HAVE CALLED, MORTAL. YOU HAVE CALLED...
...AND I HAVE ANSWERE
73G007

I HAVE BEEN TRAPPED--
TRAPPED FOR A THOUSAND YEARS AND MORE--
AWAITING A CHANCE TO SOAR FREE ONCE AGAIN!
AND YOU--
YOU SHALL BE THAT CHANCE!
YOU CANNOT FREE ME, I SENSE THAT--
BUT YOU MAY GIVE MY ANGER FORM! FORM... AND POWER! YOU SHALL BE MY VESSEL...
...MY VESSEL OF REVENGE AGAINST THOR!
PLEASE--
I DON'T--
NOW OPEN YOUR MIND TO ME--AND FEEL MY POWER FILL YOUR LUNGS, YOUR VEINS, YOUR VERY FLESH!
FEEL POWER BEYOND ANYTHING YOU HAVE EVER KNOWN, AS YOU BEGIN TO CHANGE...
...CHANGE...
31

...AND SO THE CHANGE CAME UPON HIM, CAUSING HIS BONES TO LENGTHEN, HIS MUSCLES TO INCREASE IN SIZE. HE TRIED TO STAND, AND--
--AH! LOOK AT THE SKIES-- HOW DARK IT IS! IT GROWS LATE, AND GOOD VIKING CHILDREN NEED SLEEP, TO HAVE STRENGTH FOR THE COMING DAY.
WE MUST FINISH OUR TALE ANON.
HUH? BUT--
YOU CAN'T STOP NOW!
WE'RE NOT TIRED! SLEEP--PAH! IT'S FOR WOMEN! WE WANT TO HEAR OF THE MONSTER!
DID THE GODSTORM GET ITS REVENGE? WHAT HAPPENED WITH THE TROLLS?
TELL ME WHAT THE MONSTER WAS LIKE--A TEN-FOOT OGRE? A GIANT? DID ODIN PUNISH THOR?
WE HAVE TALKED ENOUGH FOR ONE DAY. AN ELDER LIKE ME NEEDS HIS REST, EVEN IF YOU YOUNGLINGS DO NOT.
AND A VIKING IS PATIENT, AS WELL AS DETERMINED.
SOON ENOUGH, THE RUNES WILL REVEAL THE OUTCOME OF THE EVENTS WE HAVE SEEN...
...AND WE SHALL DISCOVER WHAT WILL TRANSPIRE...
...TOGETHER!
NEXT: The Tale of the Mighty Thor, and the Man Called TORRENT
32

MARVEL MASTERS
THE DAWN OF
KURT BUSIEK

By Mike Conroy

MARVEL MASTERS
THE DAWN OF KURT BUSIEK

By Mike Conroy

Born in Boston, Massachusetts in 1960, **Kurt Busiek** initially made a name for himself with letters he wrote to comics during the late 1970s. This, as he explained, gave him a profile with people he would subsequently approach for work. "As one editor told me, if they saw a Busiek letter in the pile, they knew that they could use that, at least, even if most of the mail was incoherent. So on that small level, at least, they thought of me as someone who wrote stuff they could use. That made them readier to give me a listen when I was pitching stuff, which gave me a leg up on the other guys out there pitching.

ON THE TRIP BACK TO NEW YORK, A CHANCE ENCOUNTER LED LUCAS TO REALIZE--
--THAT IF HIS NEWFOUND POWERS COULD GET HIM OUT OF JAIL--MAYBE THOSE POWERS COULD KEEP HIM OUT OF JAIL.
A NEW NAME--A COSTUME--AND HE BECAME...
LUKE CAGE HERO FOR HIRE
AND FROM THEN ON, THINGS WERE GONNA BE GOOD.

The first Marvel Super Heroes Kurt Busiek ever wrote professionally for: *Power Man and Iron Fist!*

"It also taught me, over time, to think critically about structure and character and pacing and any number of other things," he added. "In writing letters of comment, I had to articulate my thoughts, and that made me analyse the books more clearly than I otherwise might have, and that was a learning experience too."

His first professional work was a seven-page back-up in 1982's **Green Lantern #162** but he swiftly jumped from DC to Marvel, where he became the regular writer of **Power Man & Iron Fist** [1983's #80 being his first issue]. As Busiek explained, following his **Green Lantern** sale, "I sold a script to Marvel for a **Power Man & Iron Fist** fill-in that would end up being the first issue of a 12-issue run, and that was my first ongoing series, and I just kept going from there."

The end of his **Power Man & Iron Fist** run found him back at DC where, among other titles, he wrote **Justice League of America**, **Red Tornado** and **Legend of Wonder Woman**. He also contributed a story to a 1984 issue of **Zot!**, an Eclipse Comics title written by his longtime friend and future **Understanding Comics** author **Scott McCloud**.

That work for Eclipse led three years later to **The Liberty Project**, co-created with penciller **James W Fry**. It was a series about a superteam made of reformed villains, a theme he would return to a decade later while at Marvel. "I think we had a distinctive concept and some lively characters, all of whom were built around strong enough personality cores to be vivid and memorable. We had a lot of energy, which came through on the page, and I was reasonably in control of my craft as a writer, so the book was clear and readable - and fun, in an era when darkness was starting to overtake everything. And we didn't fall into any formula trap; we wanted to keep things changing, keep things from ever being predictable. Had we continued, I think we'd have kept it up - we had plans that would have thrown in regular surprises and status quo changes for another 25 issues or so.

"On the other hand, we had a lousy title – **The Liberty Project** isn't exactly a grabber, and its meaning only becomes clear after you've read the book and had it explained – and had the bad luck to premiere at around the same time as **Suicide Squad**, a DC book with a similar concept. And we were kind of raw; it's an unpolished book, and we were caught in the middle, perception-wise: Too mainstream to be an indie book, and too far from the mainstream (in terms of our lack of polish and our publisher) to attract a mainstream audience that could find stuff to satisfy them on the Marvel and DC racks – notably **Mike Barr's Batman and the Outsiders**, which had the kind of script approach I was doing my best to emulate, and [artists] **Jim Aparo** and **Alan Davis** to boot. So while we might have been able to win readers over with distinctiveness and spirit given enough time, we didn't have the chance to get enough of them to sample the series before it died."

When **The Liberty Project** folded after eight issues, the writer moved back to Marvel where he contributed to the humour title, **What the...?!** before becoming editor of **Open Space**. It was through this science fiction anthology, which he launched for Marvel in 1989, that he first encountered **Alex Ross**. The artist - who drew an ultimately unpublished story for the comic - would later show Busiek a project he was developing; one that would eventually become **Marvels**.

... UNTIL THAT HAND BEGINS TO CRACKLE--TO GLOW--
SHKOW!
--UNTIL IT BECOMES LIKE UNTO--
--A THING OF IRON!

Open Space was axed after only four issues and Busiek would spend the next few years writing fill-ins and text features for Marvel as well as other publishers. Asked to contribute to Eclipse's **Miracleman: Apocrypha**, he approached Ross to draw his story. That didn't happen but the artist did show him his idea for a painted superhero anthology book simply called "Marvel".

The writer suggested showing the Marvel heroes from the point of view of a

normal citizen in the Marvel Universe. The revised proposal was sent to Marvel, where editor **Tom DeFalco** commented, "Don't do the stories about the heroes. Do the stories about the events." Thus was born **Marvels**, a 1993 four-parter spotlighting the major happenings in the Marvel Universe from the 1940s to 1972.

The title rocketed both Ross and Busiek into the top echelon of comics creators but, as the writer remarked soon after, nothing much had changed. "I'm still doing miniseries, one-shots. Admittedly I'm doing miniseries on a higher scale. I'm doing **Youngblood: Year One** instead of **The Legend of Wonder Woman**."

But by 1995 things had started to improve. Busiek launched **Untold Tales of Spider-Man**, a Marvel series in which he unveiled stories occurring between the early **Stan Lee/Steve Ditko** issues of **Amazing Spider-Man**. It gained him much acclaim as did **Kurt Busiek's Astro City**. Published through Image Comics by WildStorm's creator-owned Homage imprint, the comic was conceived in collaboration with series artist **Brent Anderson**. Ross was also involved; visualising all the characters and painting the covers.

Described by Busiek as a homage to the Bronze Age (1970s) comics he used to read as a teenager, **Astro City** features parallels to heroes and villains from other Super Hero universes. Discussing his approach to the series, he said, "I don't place a lot of parody or satire of other worlds in it - I'm far more concerned with ideas, with what we can do with the superhero genre beyond what's usually done. I'm not making up the characters to be stand-ins for other guys; there are archetypal similarities, but not much more than that. All the guys who think the Confessor is 'my Batman', for instance, don't think it through enough to see that we couldn't tell that story with Batman - it depends on the Confessor being a very, very different guy.

"So we have shadowy vigilantes and a pantheon of heroes and flying, caped wonders and heroic families and monsters and tricksters and armoured heroes and mythic heroes and more; but we're more interested in telling people stories than in doing our version of Marvel's or DC's characters. If we really wanted to do that, Marvel and DC would be happy to let us use the real guys," the writer added.

While **Astro City** continues to be published (now through DC, which acquired WildStorm in 1999), it appears only erratically, a victim of the health issues that have plagued Busiek over the past few years. Describing the series as having a very different kind of story structure and being a very different kind of thing to write, he explained, "The difficulty I've been having writing **Astro City** has to do with my chronic health problems. I have a chronic sinus infection, and when I've got that going on in my head, it's harder for me to concentrate on the kind of delicate balance that a character-based series like **Astro City** requires. It's not a matter of the craft of structuring out the page or pacing out the issue, it's a matter of setting up everything you need to know about the character, so that when you do start asking the 'So, how do you feel about that?' questions, everything is in place so that the audience can react in sympathy, or out of sympathy with the character, depending on what's needed for the story. That's a trickier piece of craft. I wouldn't say it's better or worse, it's simply a different approach. And when I'm ill, it's an approach that I am simply not capable of delivering on.

"When I'm dealing with a sinus infection I can sit there and spend two solid weeks working on an **Astro City** story and getting nowhere - and I've done it. Whereas with **Avengers**, I can always fallback on 'what happens next,' he added, referring to the Marvel series he relaunched in tandem with artist **George Pérez** in 1998. "That the themes and character ramifications and looks into the human condition are the subtext in Avengers, and they kind of happen naturally along the way. In **Astro City** they are the text, and I have to do them consciously. And with my health situation the way it is I can't always do that."

Above: The cover to the popular *Untold Tales of Spider-Man #1*, 1995. Below: The Defenders are unexpectedly reunited in *Defenders #1*, 2001.

By the turn of the century, Busiek's name was seemingly everywhere. He had written **Velocity** for WildStorm, **The Wizard's Tale** and **Shattered Image** for Image itself and **Ninjak** for Valiant. At Marvel he'd not only rebooted **Avengers** and **Iron Man** in 1998 but the previous year he'd also returned to his Liberty Project concept to introduce a team of reformed supervillains in **Thunderbolts** and created an epic look at the history of the Earth's Mightiest Heroes in the 12-issue **Avengers Forever**.

Then, in 2000, he got together with a band of other creators – among them Pérez and writer **Mark Waid** - to form the comics brand Gorilla. A short-lived enterprise that published under the Image umbrella, it saw the release of two creator-owned titles written by Busiek: **Shockrockets** and **Superstar: As seen on TV**, both conceived in collaboration with artist **Stuart Immonen**.

Moving into the new millennium co-writing such Marvel limited series as a 2001 **Defenders** 12-parter, 2002's six-issue **The Order** and the six-issue **Avengers/Thunderbolts** (2004), Busiek also created **The Power Company** for DC. Pencilled by **Tom Grummett**, the title, which featured a mercenary superteam, launched in 2002 while the following year brought **Arrowsmith**, a creator-owned fantasy/alternate worlds series the writer conceived in partnership with artist **Carlos Pacheco** with whom he had worked on **Avengers Forever**.

By now highly regarded for his insightful and uncompromising yet reverential approach to Super Heroes, in 2003 Busiek ventured further into fantasy when he joined Dark Horse to relaunch **Conan's** comicbook career. Having dropped all his regular Marvel work, he was to write the adventures of **Robert E Howard's** archetypal sword and sorcery hero for the next three years, but stories of spandex-clad crimefighters would remain a significant part of his output.

Prior to taking on **Conan**, he once again teamed up with Pérez, this time for one of the most eagerly awaited comics of the previous 20 years. Originally announced in 1979 with Pérez as illustrator, **JLA/Avengers** was continuously delayed by various disagreements between Marvel and DC but finally saw the light of day in 2003. The four-parter was a huge commercial success but, putting his career in perspective, Busiek commented, "One of my last 'fan press' jobs before breaking in as a pro was writing for a magazine, **Comics Feature** – and I wound up writing (or maybe just editing) the news page that announced the crossover, lo those many years ago. To have gone from there to being the guy tapped to write it has been quite a journey, and nothing I ever expected."

In recent years, Busiek has signed exclusively to DC for which he has written 2004's highly regarded Immonen-drawn **Superman: Secret Identity** four-parter as well as **Action Comics**, **JLA** and **Aquaman: Sword of Atlantis**. Currently the regular scripter of **Superman**, he is rightly regarded as one of the best writers of superhero comics working in the industry today.